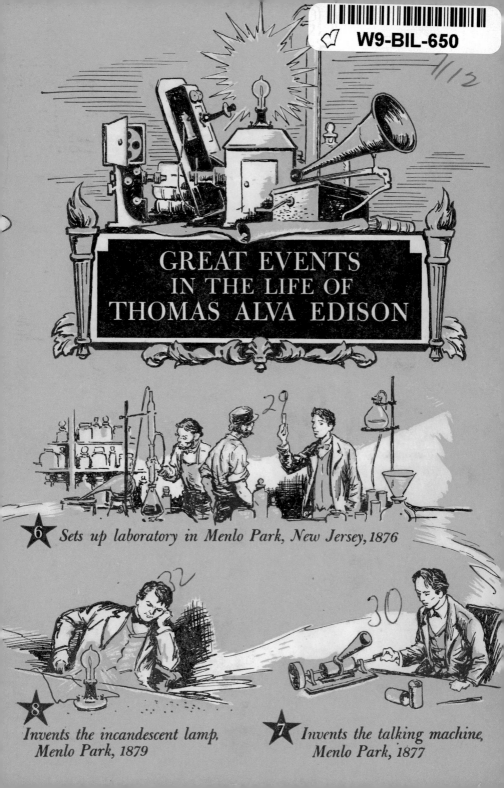

W9-BIL-650

GREAT EVENTS
IN THE LIFE OF
THOMAS ALVA EDISON

6 *Sets up laboratory in Menlo Park, New Jersey, 1876*

8 *Invents the incandescent lamp, Menlo Park, 1879*

7 *Invents the talking machine, Menlo Park, 1877*

I got this book at the Findlay
Sesquicentennial July 25 - 62.

THE STORY OF
Thomas Alva Edison

"Thomas A. Edison did more than any other man to make this world an easier, pleasanter, better world to live in.... In him were combined a phenomenal mind, a tremendous energy, and, even up to his declining years, an almost boyish enthusiasm for the successful solving of the problems of the moment."—GEORGE EASTMAN

"You put too much water in the boiler, you crazy young one"

THE STORY OF
Thomas Alva Edison

By ENID LAMONTE MEADOWCROFT

Illustrated by HARVE STEIN

PUBLISHERS Grosset & Dunlap NEW YORK

To

MRS. MARION EDISON OSER

and

HON. CHARLES EDISON

who have so graciously shared with the author
their memories of their famous father

COPYRIGHT, 1952, BY ENID LAMONTE MEADOWCROFT
The Story of Thomas Alva Edison
PRINTED IN THE UNITED STATES OF AMERICA
Library of Congress Catalog Card No. 52–11068

Contents

Illustrations

[*vii*]

ILLUSTRATIONS

THE STORY OF
Thomas Alva Edison

*"Last one in the water's a mud puppy!" Al
cried over his shoulder*

CHAPTER ONE

A Strange Experiment

IT WAS a lovely summer afternoon. The sun shone on the little Michigan town of Port Huron and on the Edisons' big white house, far out at the edge of town.

Four boys walked slowly along the dusty road which led from the house to the St. Clair River, only a short distance away. Suddenly the smallest boy began to run.

"Last one in the water's a mud puppy!" he cried over his shoulder. "A slimy, wall-eyed mud puppy!"

Michael Oates, the tallest boy, smiled slowly.

"Hey, Al," he called. "Wait a minute! It's too hot to hurry!"

[*3*]

But young Thomas Alva Edison kept right on running. Jim Clancy and Sam House sprinted after him. So Mike ran, too.

Al reached the riverbank first. He pulled off his blue shirt and long pantaloons. Then he raced to the end of an old dock, and dived into the clear cool water.

Coming to the surface, he turned and swam back toward shore. Jim and Sam were already in the river. But Mike was still on the dock.

"Mike's it!" Al called, tossing his wet brown hair back from his eyes. "Mud puppy! Mud puppy! Mike's the—"

He ducked and shouted with laughter, as Mike leaped through the air and landed with a splash almost on top of him.

For nearly an hour he and the three other boys swam and dived and played tricks on one another in the water. Then they climbed out and sprawled on the dock to rest and to dry themselves in the sun.

Al lay on his back, staring up at the sky, and listening to the sounds all around him. The sawmills down the river made a drowsy, humming noise as they cut up great trees from the Michigan forests. From a shipyard not far away came the dull pounding of a workman's hammer.

A schooner with great white sails passed, on her way north to Lake Huron. And the voices of the men on her deck drifted over the water. Then a big gray gull flew overhead, crying harshly.

The boys watched the bird wing its way over

the river to the little village of Sarnia, on the Canadian shore.

"Wish I could fly like that gull," Mike drawled. "I'd go right down the river to Detroit, so's I could see what a big city looks like. Or else I'd fly out west and hunt buffalo."

"I wouldn't," Al exclaimed. "I'd fly around here in Port Huron when folks were coming out of church and scare them half to death."

Jim chuckled. "You'd both have to grow wings first," he remarked. "Nothing stays up in the air without wings."

"Balloons do," Al declared, sitting up to scratch a mosquito bite on his ankle. "They can take a basket 'way up, with people in it, and animals, too."

"What keeps them up in the air?" Sam asked.

"Gas," Al replied. "Hydrogen gas. It's lighter than air, so when a balloon's filled with gas, it floats and—"

Jim interrupted him. "Say, how do you know so much when you're only ten and don't even go to school?" he asked.

[6]

"I learn it out of books," Al said with a grin. "I've got a new book now that tells about all kinds of experiments. And I'm starting a fine laboratory down in our cellar, so—"

"Starting a what?" Sam broke in with a puzzled frown.

"A laboratory," Al repeated, hugging his knees. "A place where you make experiments. Mike and I have collected nearly sixty bottles for it already. And I'm filling them up with all sorts of things that I'm going to need. Do you want to see them?"

Sam shrugged his shoulders. "Might as well stop in and have a look," he said. "I've got to get started home, anyway."

"Me, too," Jim added.

So the boys scrambled to their feet. They dressed quickly and set off for the Edisons' house.

There was no one in sight when they went through the front gate. Mrs. Edison was upstairs, writing a letter to her married daughter, Tannie. And Hannah, the hired girl, was in the kitchen making bread. Al led the way around the house and down the outside cellar steps.

The big cellar was cool and dark and musty-smelling. Bins of onions and a barrel of potatoes stood in one corner. In the opposite corner, near a little window, there was an untidy-looking table.

A pitcher of water and two dirty glasses stood close together on the table. Near them lay a ball of string, a dead frog, a knife, three half-burned candles, matches, and a spoon.

There were two rickety shelves over the table. On each shelf was a row of bottles of different sizes and shapes.

Mike knew all about this laboratory, for he lived with the Edisons and helped with the chores. But Sam and Jim looked around curiously. "Why have you marked each bottle 'Poison' and put a skull and crossbones on it?" Jim asked.

"So no one will fool with them," Al answered. "They've got valuable things in them. There's cotton in this one. And beeswax in this one. And baking soda in this one. And—"

He hesitated and took two bottles down from the top shelf. "And Seidlitz powders in these," he added thoughtfully.

"What do Seidlitz powders do?" Sam asked.

"They make gas if you mix them in water," Al replied slowly. Suddenly he swung around. His gray eyes were shining with excitement.

"Hey, I've just thought of something!" he exclaimed. "If anyone drank enough of this stuff he'd be filled with gas. And I'll bet he'd float right up in the air, just like a balloon."

"Could he fly?" Sam asked eagerly.

"Maybe," Al answered. "Want to try it?"

"Not me," Sam exclaimed decidedly.

"But you said you wanted to fly," Al insisted. "So did you, Mike. Listen. We'll go outdoors so you won't bump your head, and I'll mix this stuff up in some water. When it fizzes, you—"

"I don't want to try it," Mike broke in, looking very unhappy. "Anyway, I've got to finish cleaning the chicken coop before your pa comes home."

He started up the stairs. Jim grinned.

"Mike's scared," he called out. "He's thirteen and bigger than any of us. And he's just an old coward."

"I am not," Mike protested, coming back to join the other boys.

"Then try it," Al urged. "It'll be a wonderful experiment, Mike. People will be talking about it all over town. Come on, try it. Don't be scared."

He turned back to the table and uncorked both bottles. Quickly he put four teaspoonfuls of powder from the bigger bottle into one dirty glass. And four teaspoonfuls of powder from the smaller bottle into another glass.

"You bring that pitcher of water outside, Jim," he commanded. And, with a glass in each hand, he went up the cellar stairs.

The other boys followed close behind him. They watched breathlessly while he added water to each glass and then poured the mixture back and forth.

"Golly, see it fizz!" Sam exclaimed. "That ought to make you fly right over the house, Mike. Are you really going to drink it?"

"Sure he is!" Al declared. "His stomach will be so full of gas it will lift him 'way up in the air." He thrust the glass at Mike. "Here, Mike! Drink it! Quick, before it stops fizzing!"

Poor Mike! He didn't want to be called a coward, and he did want to please Al. For he thought Al Edison was the nicest boy in all Port Huron. And the smartest.

Bravely he took the glass. Shutting his eyes, he gulped down the foaming liquid. Then he opened his eyes and gasped and made a dreadful face.

Al reached for the empty glass. He studied Mike intently for a moment.

"How do you feel?" he asked hopefully. "As if something's going to lift you right off the ground?"

Mike was breathing heavily. He shook his head. Suddenly he looked at Al in dismay.

"Al!" he gasped. "If—if I do go up, how'll I ever get down again?"

"Just grab a branch of that pine tree as you float by," Al said, gazing at him steadily. "You're close enough to it. Come on, Mike.

[12]

Hold your arms out now, and try to fly."

Mike coughed and put his hand on his stomach. He felt very queer indeed. Maybe he really was going to fly. Obediently he raised his arms.

"Wave them!" Al commanded excitedly. "No, don't walk! You're full of gas now! Flap your arms like wings and fly!"

Mike swallowed hard. His face was pale. Feebly he flapped his arms. His feet stayed firmly on the ground.

Al watched him flap his arms once more. Then he shook his head.

"That's one experiment that isn't going to work," he said sadly to Jim and Sam. "I guess I didn't give him enough powder. Nothing's going to happen at all."

But the very next moment something did. Mike doubled up and cried out with pain. He dropped to the ground and rolled over groaning. He was very sick!

There was nothing Sam or Jim could do to help him, so they took to their heels. Al raced for the house.

"Mother!" he shouted at the top of his lungs. "Mother! Mike's dying! Mother! Mother! Come quick!"

CHAPTER TWO

Mrs. Edison Forgets

AL SAT up in bed. He turned his pillow over, for one side of it was wet with tears.

His legs still smarted where his mother had whipped him with her willow switch, to teach him not to experiment on his friends. He was hungry because he had been sent to bed without any supper. But, worst of all, he was worried about Mike.

Climbing out of his high-backed bed, he picked up his pantaloons, which lay on a chair near by. From one of the pockets he pulled the new jackknife which his grown-up brother, Pitt, had given him. Then he opened his door quietly and tiptoed to Mike's little room at the end of the hall.

[*15*]

Mike lay curled up in bed, with a sheet tucked around him, and his eyes tightly shut. Timidly Al touched him on the shoulder.

"Mike," he whispered. "How do you feel now? Are you better?"

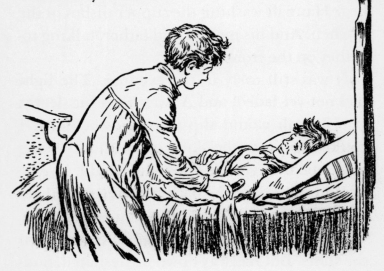

Mike opened one eye and grinned. "Sure," he said softly. "My stomach ain't hurting hardly at all any more. Don't you ever try to make me fly again, though."

Al shook his head. "I won't," he promised. "Here, take this. It's yours because I made you so sick."

[16]

He thrust the jackknife into Mike's hand. Hurrying off before Mike could thank him, he started down the hall to his own room.

At the head of the stairs, he stopped for a moment with his hand on the railing. He could hear Hannah washing the supper dishes in the kitchen. And his mother and father, talking together on the front porch.

It was still early in the evening. The light had not yet faded, and Al was not a bit sleepy.

"Hannah would slip me some cookies if I could get into the kitchen without being seen," he thought. "I know she would. Maybe I could sneak into the back parlor, too, and get something to read."

Slowly and quietly he began to creep down the stairs. But halfway down he hesitated. Suddenly it didn't seem quite fair to him that he should spend the evening with a book and cookies.

After all, his mother had had a dreadful time taking care of poor Mike. His father had had to do all Mike's chores, after a hard day's work in his grain-and-feed store.

[*17*]

"And it was all my fault," Al thought, as he stopped on the middle stair.

With a little sigh, he turned around, crept back to his room, and lay down on his bed.

A robin chirped drowsily in the pine tree just outside his open window. And the murmur of his parents' voices still sounded from the porch. Though Al didn't know it, they were talking about him.

"Sometimes I don't know what to do with that boy," Mrs. Edison was saying at that very moment. "He's not like Pitt or Tannie when they were growing up. I don't think he's really mischievous, Samuel. But he's up to some outlandish thing every minute that his nose isn't buried in a book."

"He gets himself into plenty of trouble, too," Mr. Edison remarked. Suddenly he laughed. "Do you remember the time he tried to hatch out goose eggs by sitting on them, when we lived in Ohio?" he asked.

"Yes," replied his wife with a smile. "And the time he built a fire in the barn to find out where smoke came from."

[*18*]

"And the barn burned to the ground," Mr. Edison added. He pulled a newspaper from his pocket. Then, with a twinkle in his eyes, he asked, "Why don't we send him to school again, Nancy? It might be good for him."

"Not the Port Huron school," Mrs. Edison declared firmly.

Mr. Edison chuckled. He knew very well what his wife thought of the Port Huron school and its teacher. But he liked to tease her sometimes.

He unfolded his copy of the *Port Huron Commercial,* which was dated August 25, 1857. Settling back in his chair, he began to read.

Mrs. Edison picked up the knitting which lay in her lap. Her rocking chair creaked. Her needles clicked. And her thoughts turned to the time, three years earlier, when Al had attended the Port Huron school.

It was just after the Edisons had moved to Michigan from the little village of Milan, Ohio. Al was seven. He had never been to school before. And he had asked so many questions that his teacher, Mr. Engle, was in despair.

What are stars made of? How can flies crawl upside down on the ceiling? Where does the wind come from? Why will water put out fire? Who found out how to make paper?

All these things and many others, little Al Edison had wanted to know. But Mr. Engle had been very busy trying to keep his one-room school in order. He had no time to answer Al's questions and he found the boy a great nuisance.

At last Al's mother had decided that her son would learn faster if she taught him at home.

"It's a lucky thing for us all that I was a schoolteacher once," she said to her husband now, as she rocked back and forth on the porch.

"It certainly is," agreed Mr. Edison, looking up from his newspaper. "Why, that boy is already reading books that are too much for me! Science and history and—"

"And he's understanding them, too," Mrs. Edison broke in. "But he isn't spending all his time on books, Sam. There's all that junk he's collecting in bottles down in the cellar. It worries me. I'm going to talk to him about it right now, if he's still awake."

She rolled up her knitting and went into the house. When she reached Al's room she found his bed empty.

Al stood beside his washstand near the window. He held a glass full of water in one hand and a piece of paper in the other. There was a puddle on the floor near his feet. And his nightshirt was wet. He turned around eagerly when he heard his mother's step.

"Look!" he exclaimed, before she could speak. "I got out of bed to get a drink, and I started fooling around, and look what I found out!"

He laid the paper over the top of the glass and held it in place firmly with the palm of one hand. Then he tipped the glass upside down and moved his hand away.

"See!" he said. "The water stays in the glass! What holds it there, Mother? It can't be just the paper!"

[21]

"See!" he said. "The water stays in the glass!"

Mrs. Edison shook her head. She was vexed because Al had not stayed in bed. But she was also interested in what he was doing.

"I don't know what holds the water there," she replied. And, coming closer, she watched curiously while Al moved the glass around in a circle.

"I can even jiggle it—and the water stays in!" Al exclaimed. He turned the glass right side up and upside down and jiggled it gently.

A few drops leaked out from under the rim. Suddenly the paper fell and the water splashed to the floor. Mrs. Edison stepped back hastily.

Al reached at once for the blue china pitcher so that he could fill the glass again. But his mother shook her head.

"That's enough of that, Al," she declared, brushing some drops of water from her long gray skirt. "Mop up the floor right away with one of those towels. Then put on a dry night-shirt and get to bed."

"Yes'm," Al said meekly. "I will. But what kept the water in the glass so long?"

His mother laughed. "I don't know," she ad-

[23]

mitted, as she pulled a dry nightshirt from a bureau drawer. "But I do know that you'll never be happy until you find the answer. You can't do it tonight, though. Come on, now, get to bed quickly."

She watched Al mop up the water and waited until he was safely in bed. Then she said good night and went downstairs. Not until late that evening did she remember why she had gone to Al's room.

"Those dratted bottles!" she exclaimed to her husband, who sat with her in the back parlor, reading. "I went all the way upstairs to tell Al that he must clear them out of the cellar tomorrow. And I clean forgot about it."

Mr. Edison smiled. "Oh, let him keep them awhile longer," he suggested. "He'll probably be tired of playing with them in a few days, and he'll throw them out without being told."

But Mr. Edison was mistaken. Before long Al and Mike had picked many more bottles out of junk piles and rubbish barrels all over town. And strange things were going on down in the Edisons' cellar!

CHAPTER THREE

Al Is Worried

MRS. EDISON set one chocolate-covered cake aside and began to ice the other one. She spoke to Hannah, who stood at the kitchen sink, washing yellow mixing-bowls and shiny tin pans.

"We'll have the smaller cake for supper, Hannah," she said. "When the frosting hardens, Al can take the other one over to Mrs. Boomer's house for the church social."

Hannah nodded. "I wish he'd bring in some wood for the cookstove first," she remarked, as she pumped some water into the teakettle. "He ain't filled the lamps yet, either, Mrs. Edison. It seems to me like he forgets to do his chores now 'most every—"

[25]

She jumped as a muffled bang sounded from the cellar.

"Land sakes!" she exclaimed. "What's that? He'll blow this house up yet!"

Mrs. Edison dropped her spoon and pulled open the door which led to the cellar.

"Al!" she called anxiously. "Are you all right?"

"Sure," Al shouted back. "I was just trying

to see if I could explode some hydrogen with electricity. And I could!"

There was an instant's silence. Then Al yelled, "Hey, Mother! If I had enough hydrogen I might be able to blow up the whole world—just with one electric spark."

"Well, you're not going to blow up the world this afternoon," his mother replied. "Put your things away and come upstairs. Hannah needs wood for the cookstove. And you forgot to fill the lamps before you did your lessons."

"I'll be up in a minute," Al called.

He sighed and ran his fingers through his thick brown hair. He didn't mind bringing in stovewood from the shed behind the house. But he hated taking care of the lamps.

"Smelly old things," he muttered. "I'll bet Mike would fill them for me, if he wasn't working at the feed store."

Bending down, he gathered up the pieces of a small cardboard house which lay scattered over the cellar floor. With a pleased smile he looked them over. Then he tossed them into a rubbish barrel. Reaching for a sheet of paper which lay on the table, he wrote carefully: APRIL 10, 1858. *Filled cardbord house with hydrogen gas and exsploded it with electric sparks. Got sparks by rubing glass hard with peice of rubber. Good experiment.*

He stuck the sheet of paper into a bulging, untidy-looking scrapbook. Then he put all his equipment away in a brand-new cupboard. Locking the cupboard carefully, he stuck the key in his pocket and started for the kitchen. Three minutes later he was scraping out the pan which had held the chocolate frosting.

His mother laughed when she saw him. For his hair stuck out in every direction. His face was streaked with dirt. There were big yellow stains on his shirt. And he had a long, jagged tear in his pantaloons.

"Al, you're a sight!" she exclaimed. "You'll have to clean up before you take that cake to Mrs. Boomer's."

"I will," Al promised. He licked the spoon and glanced up at his mother. "Can I have some money?" he asked hopefully.

"Money!" his mother repeated in amazement. "Why, Pitt gave you a whole silver dollar when he and his wife were here on Sunday! What on earth have you done with it?"

"Spent it all on mercury to make a barometer," Al replied, scraping the frosting-pan nois-

ily. "Now I need more money to buy hydrochloric acid and—"

"Then you'll just have to earn it," his mother broke in. She took the pan away from him and set it in the sink. "Come on, son,"

[*29*]

she added. "Get to work on the lamps. They're out on the back porch, waiting for you."

Al gave the spoon a final lick. He handed it to Hannah, and stepped out on the back porch.

It had rained all the morning, but the sun now shone brightly. A brisk wind tossed the bare branches of the apple and pear trees in the big orchard near the barn. It ruffled the feathers of the white chickens which were pecking in the yard.

Al stared at the chickens without even seeing them. He was worrying about money. And about how he could earn some to buy the materials he needed for his laboratory. If he couldn't buy materials, he couldn't do experiments. If he couldn't do experiments, he couldn't find out all the things he wanted to know. Suddenly he had an idea.

"That's it!" he exclaimed under his breath. "The ice on the lake is almost gone, and—"

A long telescope stood in the corner of the Edison back porch. In a moment it was tucked firmly under Al's right arm.

"Be back in a minute," he called, as he stuck

his head in the door. And, clearing the porch steps with one jump, he raced across the yard toward a high wooden tower.

His father had built this tower, hoping that people would pay to climb to the top, to see the fine view. But only a few had been willing to climb up the long, winding stairs.

Now Al ran up them like a squirrel, while the tower swayed back and forth in the wind. Standing with his feet wide apart, to keep his balance, he raised his telescope to his right eye.

He did not look at the great forest which lay a mile or so to the west. Nor at the thick grove of pine trees which grew just south of the Edisons' house.

He did not even look east toward Canada, to see if he could spot any Indians from the reservation near Sarnia. Instead, he looked directly north, past old Fort Gratiot, just across the road, and all the way to Lake Huron.

Although it was April, a few jagged cakes of ice still bobbed about in the blue water. Several sailboats were moving across the lake. Two southbound schooners were just entering the St. Clair River. And, half a mile behind them, a little steamboat was puffing along steadily.

Al smiled when he saw the steamboat. This was what he had been looking for! He would finish his chores quickly and carry the chocolate cake to Mrs. Boomer's. Then he'd get to the Butler Street wharf before the steamboat put in, to leave passengers. And perhaps he could earn a dollar or more, carrying the passengers' carpetbags over to the hotel.

"Then I'd have enough to buy hydrochloric acid and some test tubes, too," he thought joyfully, as he put his telescope away on the back porch a little later. "Now for those lamps!"

He picked up the big can of kerosene standing near the door. And he turned to the bench on which his mother had set the lamps. Balancing the heavy can carefully, he poured the smelly oil into each lamp. Then he trimmed the greasy wicks and polished each sooty chimney.

When that was finished he carried the lamps into the house and placed them in the different

[32]

rooms where they belonged. The last one belonged in the kitchen.

"There," Al said, setting it down on the
table with a thud. "That poky job's done! I

should think there'd be a better way to light
houses than with these greasy old things."

"Too bad we don't live in a city, where
there's gas," Hannah said, with a sniff. "I sup-
pose that even if we had gaslights, you'd say
there ought to be something better!"

"Guess I would," Al declared. "Gas can kill
you if you breathe it. It's even more dangerous
than these old coal-oil lamps."

[*33*]

Hannah put her hands on her hips. "Will you quit worrying, now, about better ways to light a house, and go get me some stove-wood?" she asked impatiently.

"All right, Crosspatch," Al said with a grin. And he ran out of the back door and toward the woodshed.

It did not take him long to fill the woodbox, or to change his clothes and deliver the chocolate cake. Then he set off, whistling gaily, for the Butler Street wharf.

He was not whistling, however, when he came home late that afternoon. And his face was sober as he sat down to supper that night with his mother and father. Not one passenger from the steamer had wanted a carpetbag carried to the hotel!

"I didn't earn a single penny," Al said sadly, as he finished telling his parents where he had been. "And I need money for chemicals and things, worse than a skunk needs friends."

His father smiled.

"I know a way that you and Mike can work together to earn lots of money," he declared, spearing some fried potatoes with his fork.

Al swallowed a mouthful of ham so quickly that he nearly choked.

"How?" he asked eagerly.

"Well," said his father, "I'll tell you." And he began to describe his plan.

Long before he had finished speaking, Al's eyes were shining. Already, in his own mind, the boy was buying everything he would ever need for his laboratory in the cellar.

CHAPTER FOUR

A Wonderful Chance

THE old white horse clip-clopped slowly down the dusty, tree-shaded street. Mike walked at the horse's head. Al rode in the little cart behind, looking hopefully toward the houses on either side of him.

Cupping his hands around his mouth, he shouted loudly, "Corn! Sweet corn! Good, fresh, sweet corn, a dime a dozen. Tom-a-a-aytoes, two bits a peck."

He jingled some coins in his pocket. Then he exclaimed, "Hey, Mike, there's old Mrs. Gray waving out of her kitchen window! I'll see what she wants."

Al jumped over the wheel, even before Mike had stopped the horse. And he ran around to

Mrs. Gray's back door. When he came back he was grinning from ear to ear.

"She'll take that last bushel of tomatoes and all the corn we have left," he announced, pulling a basket of corn from the cart. "Then we're through for the day."

Mike shook his head. "No, we ain't," he said slowly. "We've got to catch potato bugs all afternoon."

"Aw, shucks!" Al exclaimed impatiently. "I forgot those blamed bugs! There must be sixty million of them, too! I wish my father had never thought of this truck-gardening business, Mike."

Mike grinned and swung a heavy bushel basket of tomatoes to the ground. "You liked it fine last year," he said, dragging his arm across his hot forehead. "Raising vegetables and selling them seemed a mighty easy way to earn money then, didn't it?"

"Yep, it did," Al agreed. "And we've made lots of money at it, too. But I don't get enough time to do my experiments now and—"

He stopped and cocked his head to one side.

[*37*]

"Hey, Mike!" he exclaimed. "Do you hear music?"

Mike listened for an instant. Then he nodded. "Drums and a fife," he said. "It's a long way off, though."

"It means the Panorama's in town!" Al

cried excitedly. "Let's finish up here and get home in a hurry. We can catch some of those bugs before dinner, and let the rest go till tomorrow and—"

"And see the Panorama this afternoon?" Mike asked eagerly.

"Sure," Al replied. Picking up the basket of corn, he ran around the house. Mike fol-

lowed him, lugging the tomatoes. Soon both boys were back in the cart, riding home as fast as the old horse could take them.

That afternoon they put on their copper-toed boots and Sunday clothes. Then they hurried to town to join the crowd which was streaming into a big tent set up near Court House Square.

They found seats near the front, and a moment later Sam House and Jim Clancy sat down on the bench just behind them.

Jim stared at the bright blue banner which hung over the platform, and read the words printed on it:

PANORAMA OF THE GREAT WEST

"Hey, Al," he said over Al's shoulder, "what the dickens is this panorama thing? I've never seen one before."

Al turned around. "It's a big, long, painted picture," he explained. "It unrolls right in front of you, real slow. You can see everything just as if you were riding past it in a train, and—"

"Shut up," Mike whispered, giving Al a

poke in the ribs. "Here's a man to tell us about it."

And there, just stepping out on the platform, was a tall man in a high hat, a black coat, and a bright red waistcoat. Taking off his hat, he bowed low.

"Ladies and gentlemen," he began in a loud voice. "I have the honor to present to you this afternoon the Panorama of the Great West. This marvelous, breath-taking, *stupendous* picture is more than three miles long!"

"Three miles!" someone in the crowd exclaimed aloud. And there was a buzz of excited whispering. Then the man on the platform continued his speech.

"In this magnificent Panorama we take you all the way from New Orleans to Lake Michigan! You will see slaves working in a cotton field! The majestic Mississippi River with its big steamers! The Great American Desert! Snow-capped mountains and—"

"There's going to be a prairie fire, too," Sam whispered over Al's shoulder. "And an Indian fight and—"

[*41*]

"Sh!" Al said. "I want to listen."

And listen he did, as the man continued talking. Soon the Panorama started moving slowly across the platform. Al hardly stirred

until the last few feet of painted canvas had been unrolled, nearly three hours later.

He clapped and cheered with the rest of the audience when the show was over. But he had little to say as the crowd left the tent.

"What are you so quiet about?" Sam asked,

as the boys walked slowly across the field. "Wasn't that a wonderful show?"

"Yes," said Al slowly. "But I was thinking that the picture would be a lot better if you could just see the people and animals move around."

Sam winked at Mike and nudged Jim with his elbow. Then he looked soberly at Al. "You mean if you could see them acting just as if they were alive?" he asked.

Al nodded thoughtfully. Mike burst out laughing. So did Jim and Sam. Al's face flushed.

"Maybe that could happen some day, if anybody kept experimenting long enough," he insisted.

"And maybe cows could learn to sing," Sam jeered as the boys started across the street. "Honest, Al, sometimes your ideas do sound loony."

"Lots of good ideas seem loony when you first think about them," Al retorted hotly. "Look at the electric telegraph! I'll bet everyone thought Mr. Morse was crazy when he said

[43]

he could send a message over a wire quick as lightning."

"But he did it in spite of them!" Jim added. "Hey, Al, are they going to have a telegraph operator in the new depot?"

"Don't know," Al replied, jumping up to pull a maple leaf from a low-hanging bough. "The depot's most finished, though. And I read in the newspaper that the track's laid halfway to Detroit!"

"It's sure going to be a lot faster to whiz along in a train than to travel in that poky old stagecoach," Sam declared. "My pa's going to take me to Detroit in the train as soon as the railroad's finished."

"When's that going to be?" Mike asked.

"October," Sam replied. "At least that's what my pa says."

But Sam's father was wrong. It was not until November that the Grand Trunk Railway was ready to carry passengers from Port Huron to Detroit. And one cold morning, people on horseback, in wagons, in carriages, and on foot flocked to the new depot to see the first train pull out.

[*44*]

Al and Mike were there early, for the railway station had been built at the edge of town, not far north of the Edisons' house.

Eagerly the two boys walked the length of the train. Gazing at the pictures painted on the sides of the bright yellow coaches. Jumping up to look through the narrow windows. Trying to poke their noses into the baggage car. And examining the shiny new engine, with its big red wheels and its bands of gleaming brass.

Al even started to swing himself up into the engineer's cab. But the fireman, who was tossing wood into the firebox, shouted at him angrily. So Al jumped down at once.

Blowing on his hands to warm them, he stepped back to the platform. And he looked with envy at the people who were climbing aboard to make the first trip.

"I'll tell you what, Mike," he said. "I'm going to get a ride one day on those steam cars."

"Me, too," Mike declared. Then he wandered off to speak to Jim, who was standing at the other end of the platform.

At that very moment three important-looking men came out from the depot, talking together. They stopped just behind Al and the boy could not help overhearing their conversation.

The first man spoke proudly of the fine new coaches on the train. The second man boasted that the train could run as fast as thirty miles an hour. Then the third man said, "Yes, gentlemen, but there's one thing we lack. We must get a boy somewhere to sell newspapers and candy to the passengers."

Al caught his breath. His heart almost skipped a beat. What a wonderful chance that would be for him! He could ride on the train every day. He could see the big city of Detroit. And he could be earning money for his laboratory at the same time.

Turning around quickly, he looked up at the tall man who had just spoken.

"Please, sir," he said eagerly. "I—I couldn't help hearing what you just said. If you need a boy to sell newspapers, I—I'd like the job."

The tall man smiled. "How old are you?" he asked.

"Twelve, sir," Al answered promptly. "I'll

[46]

"If you need a boy to sell newspapers,
I—I'd like the job"

be thirteen on the eleventh of February. And I wouldn't expect you to pay me any money at all. Not if I could keep what I earned selling papers and candy."

"That's fair enough," declared the tall man. He grabbed his hat as a stiff wind swooped down from the north. "What's your name?" he asked.

"Thomas Alva Edison," Al replied. "I could start working right off tomorrow morning when the train leaves at seven o'clock, if you gave me the job."

The tall man laughed. "You sound like a hustler, young fellow!" he exclaimed. "That's the kind of fellow we need! Talk it over with your parents. If they say it's all right, you can go to work tomorrow. If they don't, come back before noon today and leave word here for me, with the ticket agent."

"Yes, sir," Al cried joyfully. And he was off for home like a shot from a cannon, without even waiting to see the new train pull away from the depot.

CHAPTER FIVE

A Narrow Escape

IT WAS cold on the platform of the Grand Trunk Railway depot in Detroit. Bitter cold! Conductor Stephenson stamped his feet impatiently as he stood beside his waiting train.

At last the engine bell clanged loudly. Conductor Stephenson looked sharply up and down the platform.

"All aboard!" he shouted, though no one was in sight. " 'Board!"

He signaled to the engineer with his lantern. Then he swung himself up the high steps of the last car just as it jerked forward. Slowly, with several stops and starts, the six-thirty train to Port Huron got under way.

The three cars creaked and swayed and creaked again. The oil lamps, fastened to the

ceilings of the coach and smoking car, flick-
ered. In each car a red-hot, pot-bellied stove
sent out waves of heat. The passengers settled
themselves as comfortably as possible on the
hard, narrow, plush-covered seats.

Al stepped quickly from the baggage car
into the passenger coach, with a big armful
of newspapers and magazines. He glanced

quickly down the length of the car. Nearly
every seat was taken! Business would be good
tonight.

"Papers!" he called loudly, starting down

the aisle. "All the latest papers and magazines! *Detroit Free Press! Harper's Weekly! Youth's Companion!* Yes, sir, what will you have?"

Selling papers and magazines, making change, and joking with the passengers, he walked slowly through the swaying coach. Then he went on, into the smoking car.

He made many stops. And when he returned to the baggage car, his pocket was filled with coins. Soon he started out again, carrying a heavy basket.

"Peanuts and popcorn!" His clear voice rang out above the clatter of the wheels. "Big, fresh-roasted, double-jointed peanuts! All you can eat for a dime! Popcorn balls! Better get some if you missed your supper in Detroit! Good red apples! Not a worm in 'em! Peanuts!"

Again, many people stopped Al as he went down the aisle. Not only because they wanted something to eat. But because they liked to buy things from this friendly train-boy.

Al gave them plenty of time to look over his wares, and he had a cheerful word for everyone. When he went back to the baggage car at last, his basket was nearly empty.

More than two months had passed since he had started working as a train-boy on the Grand Trunk Railway. And he liked everything about the job.

He had made friends quickly with the train crew. Already he knew the ticket agents in every depot along the line. He thought it was fun to run his own business, without help from anyone. He was earning enough now to pay his mother seven dollars a week for board, and to buy chemicals for experiments every week, too. Best of all, he could spend nearly eight hours each day in Detroit.

Every morning, as soon as he reached that busy, noisy city, he bought the fruit, candy, nuts, and magazines which he planned to sell later. When this job was finished, he was free to do as he pleased, until it was time to get his newspapers in the late afternoon.

At first, Al had spent his time in Detroit wandering up and down the wooden sidewalks. Gaping at the high five-story office buildings. Looking into store windows. And watching people getting on and off the omnibuses which rattled over the cobblestoned streets.

Then he had discovered a large free library, where he could sit for hours, reading books on science and other subjects. He had found his way to the Detroit Locomotive Works, too.

Often he went there to talk with the workmen who were constructing new engines for the railroads. Or he stopped in at the *Detroit Free Press* building, to watch the printers set type and run the big printing presses.

Before going back to the railway station each evening, he bought supplies for his laboratory. And he picked up bundles of newspapers to sell on his return trip.

It was a fine life! Now, in the dimly lighted baggage car, Al whistled happily as he counted out the newspapers which were left in his pile.

"Only thirty-six left," he said to Bill, the big brakeman, who sat on a trunk smoking a stubby clay pipe.

"You'll sell most of them, before you get

home," Bill remarked. "Don't forget that Mr. Mackenzie wants one, when we get to Mount Clemens."

Al grinned. "I'd never forget him!" he exclaimed. "He's one of the nicest ticket agents all along the line. Hey! We're almost to Fraser! I'd better hustle!"

"Me, too," Bill said, knocking the ashes from his pipe, and getting to his feet. He put on his large, rough leather gloves. "Sure hope we don't hit no cow tonight," he added. "I'll never forget—"

But Al never heard the rest of Bill's sentence. For the brakeman's voice was drowned by the rattle of the train, as Bill opened the door and stepped outside.

Al buttoned his jacket rapidly and turned up the collar. Putting on his cap, he picked up half a dozen newspapers. When the train jerked to a stop at Fraser, he was the first person to hop off.

In spite of the cold, several people were waiting for him, eager to read the latest news. Al sold five of his papers quickly and started back to the train. At that moment an old farmer with a big lantern in his hand appeared in the doorway of the depot.

"Boy!" he shouted. "Hey, boy! Bring me a *Free Press!*"

Yanking his last newspaper from under his arm, Al darted to the station door and stepped inside. The farmer fumbled in his purse for a coin.

" 'Board!" yelled Conductor Stephenson. "All aboard!"

Al held out his hand to the farmer for his money. Thrusting it into his pocket, he raced across the platform. The train had just started. Quickly Al caught at the railing of the baggage-car steps and tried to swing himself up. But he missed his footing! The train gathered speed! Al held fast to the railing, though his feet were dragging along on the ground.

"Brakeman, grab that boy!" someone shouted. "Help him! He'll get killed!"

Bill was standing on the platform. He was just about to enter the baggage car. But he turned quickly.

[55]

"Hang on, Al," he cried. "Hang on! Watch those wheels! I'll pull you up!"

Bracing his feet wide apart on the swaying platform, Bill reached down. His powerful

hands shot out. He grasped Al firmly by the head, with one big hand over each of the boy's ears. Then he stepped back suddenly. With a quick jerk, he dragged Al to the car platform.

The train was almost up to full speed now.

[56]

Al was panting and weak with fright. He stumbled into the baggage car and sat down on a low box, with his hands over his ears. Bill followed him.

"I sure thought you were done for, bub," he said, as he peered anxiously down at the boy. "If you'd let go, you might have rolled right under the wheels."

Taking off his gloves, he eyed Al closely. "Hope I didn't hurt your ears none," he went on in a kindly voice. "I couldn't think of no other way, real quick, to get you aboard."

Al laughed shakily. "I—guess you just— saved my life!" he gasped. "That's—all! Th-thanks, Bill!"

The boy had felt something snap inside his head when the brakeman had pulled him into the train. Now his ears were ringing loudly. They ached, too.

He tried to forget the pain, however, as he counted out the papers he hoped to sell at the next station. But his ears still hurt when he reached home later that night.

"I won't tell Mother and Father about what happened at Fraser," he thought as he walked up the front steps. "It was hard enough persuading them to let me take that job on the train. I don't want them to tell me I have to quit it now, just because I almost had an accident."

Pushing open the front door, Al stepped into the wide hall.

"Hello," cried his father from the back parlor. "Glad you're safely home, boy. Did you bring me some papers?"

"Yep," Al replied cheerfully. And he took his father all the newspapers which he had not sold.

Ten minutes later Al sat in the warm, snug kitchen, eating a hot supper. As he devoured beef stew, biscuits, and apple pie, he told his mother all that he had done that day in Detroit. Then, without thinking, he covered his ears with his hands.

"What's the matter?" his mother asked anxiously. "Did your ears get frostbitten?"

"No," Al replied slowly. "They—they just ache."

"I'll warm some sweet oil," his mother said,

[58]

getting to her feet. "That will fix them up in no time."

And the warm sweet oil did ease Al's earache for a while. But, during the following weeks, the pain returned again and again.

Something had happened to twelve-year-old Thomas Alva Edison that day at Fraser, which he would never be able to forget. Something which would help to make him one of the most famous men in America.

CHAPTER SIX

Engineer Al

AL STOOD in the cab of the locomotive with his hand on the throttle. His heart pounded with excitement and his eyes were shining. For he was running the engine of the night train to Port Huron, all by himself.

He had often ridden in the locomotive cab, when there were not many passengers on the train, and when his business was poor. He had also run the engine several times. But only for a few miles at a stretch. And always under the watchful eye of the engineer.

This time, however, near the end of the run, Tim Shane had fallen asleep in a corner of the cab. So had Hank Jones, the fireman. Both men had been up all the night before, dancing at a trainmen's ball. They were snoring loudly, for they were tired out.

"And I'm not going to wake them till I get the train all the way to Port Huron," Al thought gleefully.

He reached up and pulled the whistle cord, as the train neared a crossing. Then he stuck his head out of the cab. All was clear ahead.

Al eyed the little locomotive proudly. Gray

smoke streamed from its huge smokestack. The polished brass trimmings gleamed in the May moonlight. And the big wheels made a pleasant clackety-clack as they rolled along the iron rails.

Al knew that the boiler was brimful of water, for he had filled it himself at the last water tank.

"Nothing to worry over as far as that's concerned," he thought, feeling very much pleased with himself. "Driving an engine's easy. Just wait till Mike and Jim hear about this!"

With his eyes on the track ahead and the cool night air rushing past his face, he smiled broadly. Then suddenly he gasped and ducked his head.

A cloud of black mud was coming right at him! Warm, black mud! It splashed over his hair. It ran down his cheeks. It glued his eyes shut.

Al jerked his head inside the cab and wiped his eyes quickly on his shirtsleeve. Moving the throttle, he slowed the train down to twelve miles an hour. Carefully, he stuck his head outside again.

The brass on the locomotive gleamed no longer. The engine was covered with great splotches of mud. And the huge smokestack was spouting more mud.

"The old thing's gone crazy!" Al muttered. "I'll have to wake Tim and—no, I won't, by jings! The mud's stopped!"

He stared at the smokestack in amazement. It was now sending up gray smoke as usual.

With a sigh of relief, Al gave the engine a little more steam. Wondering what had happened to the big stack, he pulled the train to a stop at the next station.

It was here that Hank Jones always climbed out on the locomotive to put oil in the oil cup on the steam chest. Al grinned when he saw that the fireman was still sleeping soundly.

In spite of his mud bath, the boy was having a wonderful time. And he didn't want either Hank or Tim to waken and take his job away from him. Picking up the oil can, he climbed out on the engine and opened the oil cup.

[*63*]

"Whisssssssh!" Out rushed a roaring blast of steam from the big steam chest.

Al jumped back, so startled that he nearly fell from the engine. Hastily he pushed down the cover of the oil cup and climbed into the cab again.

For a moment he wondered if he should wake Hank and tell him what had happened. Then he shook his head. The Port Huron depot was the next stop, and he wasn't going to give up driving the engine now.

"Guess we'll run that far without oil," he thought, as he watched for Conductor Stephenson to signal with his lantern from the back. "But I sure hope nothing else happens."

And nothing else did for a while. But just as Al was bringing the train proudly up to the depot, the smokestack spluttered suddenly. Another cloud of thick, black mud came sailing through the air!

Muttering under his breath, Al brought the train to a stop and wiped his eyes. He was feeling a little foolish and not a bit proud as he wakened Tim and Hank. With mud dripping from his hair and running down his clothes, he climbed from the cab.

The station agent and several other men had already gathered around the locomotive. The conductor and brakeman were coming to join them. And so was Mike. For he always met Al with the old horse and cart, and drove him into town to sell the evening papers.

He looked at Al now and gasped. The men all burst into roars of laughter at the sight of the mud-covered boy. And everyone began to talk at once.

One of the men declared that Al had done a good job, getting the train to Port Huron without help. The station agent complained that the train was late and said it was lucky that there hadn't been an accident. Then Bill, the brakeman, announced with a sly wink that it would take at least a week to get the engine clean.

"It'll take me a week to get clean, too," Al said, rubbing some mud from his face. "What the dickens is wrong with that smokestack, anyway?"

[65]

"You put too much water in the boiler, you crazy young one," Tim replied. "It got carried up the stack with the exhaust and it washed out all the soot. Did you fill the oil cup on the steam chest?"

"Nope," said Al. "I tried to, but so much steam came out that I—"

"Steam!" Hank shouted. "Didn't you shut off the steam before you opened that oil cup? Ain't you seen Tim do that at least a dozen times?"

Al shook his head. And all the men except one burst into another roar of laughter. This man tugged at his gray beard and looked soberly at Al.

"You'd better make sure you know what you're doing before you try running a train again, bub," he said slowly. "Otherwise someone's liable to get hurt."

Turning on his heel, the old man walked off to the omnibus, which was waiting to carry passengers to the town.

Al's face reddened. He didn't like being scolded by strangers. But as he climbed into the baggage car to get his newspapers, he told himself that the old man had been right.

"That was a fool thing to do," he said when he and Mike were riding home. "By jings, it was fun, though. And I learned something, too. Say, Mike, I don't want to go into town looking like a dirty old crow. Will you sell the papers for me tonight?"

Mike nodded and slapped Nell with the reins. "How many have you got left?" he asked.

The night was quiet and he spoke softly. Al made no reply.

"How many papers have you got left?" Mike asked again, as the omnibus from the depot rattled by.

Still Al did not answer.

Mike turned to him impatiently. "Hey, Al!" he exclaimed, raising his voice. "I've asked you twice how many papers you've got left and you don't even answer me. What's the matter? Are you getting deaf?"

"Deaf?" Al repeated, wrinkling his forehead in a worried frown. "No, of course I'm not deaf. Let me out here, Mike, will you? I'll take the short cut home and you can save time by going straight to town."

Without waiting for Mike to stop the horse, he jumped from the cart. And he set off toward home across a moonlit meadow.

Mike's last question bothered him. This was the fourth time since morning that someone had asked him if he were deaf.

"But only old people get deaf," Al told himself. "And my ears hardly ever ache any more. At least, not nearly as much as they did. I wonder—"

He stopped under a tree and listened intently. It was a lovely spring night. And he could hear insects singing quite plainly, although they did seem rather far away. Suddenly he heard an owl hoot from a branch right over his head.

Al laughed aloud. With a whoop of joy, he raced across the meadow.

"There's nothing deaf about *me*," he thought, as he ran through the orchard and up the back steps. "I just don't listen closely enough when people talk to me."

[68]

He pushed open the back door. The house was dark, for Mr. and Mrs. Edison were spending the evening with neighbors and Hannah was away.

Al fumbled about for a match and lighted the kitchen lamp. He stuck his head under the pump in the sink and washed off the black mud. Upstairs, he found a clean shirt. Then he gobbled the supper which his mother had left on the kitchen table, and went down cellar to his laboratory.

He was in a hurry to send a message over the telegraph wire which he had set up between his house and Jim Clancy's. Jim had helped him string up the wire, and make the receiving and sending instruments. Al had bought batteries. And the two boys practiced every night, telegraphing to each other in the Morse code.

Al tapped out, "Hello, Jim," on his sending key and waited for an answer. It came promptly. Soon he was tapping out the story of how he had driven the locomotive, and answering Jim's questions about it. The clicking of his telegraph key was the first sound his parents heard when they opened the front door an hour later.

"That boy ought to be asleep!" Mrs. Edison exclaimed as her husband lighted a lamp. "He has to be up at six."

Mr. Edison nodded and stepped to the head of the cellar stairs.

"Al," he boomed in his deep voice. "It's time you were in bed."

Al tapped out, "Wait," to Jim. Then he called, "Can't I stay up and practice half an hour longer?"

"Not even ten minutes longer," his father replied. "Come on, son. It's past eleven o'clock."

With a sigh, Al tapped out, "Good night," to Jim. Picking up his lamp, he went upstairs. He was not the least bit sleepy. And long after he had crawled between the sheets, he lay awake, thinking.

He was doing well with his newspaper business. So well that he had already hired two boys to sell papers for him on trains running from Port Huron to Detroit. He had more money

[70]

to spend on chemicals than ever before.

"All I need is time," he thought, turning over restlessly. "It's just foolish to spend so many hours in bed when I could be doing experiments, or learning to be a real telegraph operator. I wish I could figure out some way to make Father *want* me to stay up."

For several minutes he lay on his back, staring into the dark and thinking about this problem. Suddenly he sat bolt upright.

"I've got it!" he exclaimed with a chuckle. "Jim will have to help, but he'll laugh his head off when I tell him about it."

With another chuckle he lay down again, and pulled the covers under his chin. In an instant he was sound asleep.

CHAPTER SEVEN

A Prince and a Black Eye

M R. EDISON closed his book when he heard Al come into the house.

"Hello," he said as the boy stepped into the back parlor. "Did you have a good day?"

Al nodded. But before he could speak, his father asked quickly, "Where are my newspapers, son? Didn't you save me some?"

"Yep," Al replied, ruffling up his hair. "I did. But, to tell the truth, Father, I stopped in at Jim's for a minute on the way home. And I left them there. I could go back and get them for you, but—"

He hesitated and Mr. Edison shook his head.

"No, no, don't bother," he said. "Go and eat your supper, boy. I'll get along without the news tonight."

He reached over to turn down the lamp, which had begun to smoke. Trying not to smile, Al started for the kitchen. In the doorway, he turned.

"I could take my supper to the cellar," he suggested. "Then I could signal Jim to send us the news over the telegraph line. You could get it that way."

His father laughed. "It would take all night to get the news over *your* telegraph line!" he exclaimed.

With a sigh, he opened his book again, but he found it hard to keep his mind on what he was reading.

Like most thoughtful Americans in the year 1860, Mr. Edison was greatly worried about his country. For trouble was brewing in the United States between the South and the North. Trouble over slavery and other things.

Many people in the Southern states owned Negro slaves. They wanted the right to take their slaves with them, if they moved to the new lands which were being settled in the West.

Many people in the Northern states felt that slavery was wrong. They were determined to keep it from spreading. And they were working hard to elect Abraham Lincoln as the President of the United States. For they knew that Lincoln hated slavery and would fight against it.

"If Lincoln is elected," said the Southern leaders, "we will leave the Union and set up our own government."

"You can't do that," said the Northern leaders. "The American states are united states and we intend that they shall stay united."

Matters were going from bad to worse. There was already talk of a war between the states.

"And this certainly is no time to be without a newspaper," Mr. Edison thought, shutting his book with a bang. Getting to his feet, he strode into the kitchen where Al was talking with his mother, as he finished his supper.

"You know, Al," said Mr. Edison, "it might be a good idea to try to get some news from Jim after all. Can you start now?"

"Sure I can," Al replied, swallowing his last bite of cake quickly. With a mischievous gleam in his eyes, he pushed his chair back from the table and led the way down cellar.

Soon his telegraph instrument was clicking busily. Jim sent the news in the Morse code. Al turned the little clicks into words and wrote them down for his father.

It was slow work, but Mr. Edison read every sentence eagerly. And he looked up sharply when Mrs. Edison called from the kitchen that it was past Al's bedtime.

[75]

"Oh, let him stay up a little longer, Nancy," Mr. Edison called back. "It won't hurt him, just this once."

Al ducked his head to hide a grin. His scheme was working!

"He *wants* me to stay up," the boy thought joyfully. And he went on taking down the messages which Jim was sending.

It was nearly one o'clock that night when Al finally crawled into bed. Yet he was up at six in the morning, as wide awake as usual.

That night and the next night, Al came home without the papers. And each time, he and his father sat up very late, getting the news from Jim.

On the fourth night, however, Mr. Edison met his son at the door. Leading him to the lamp, he looked him over closely. The boy did not seem a bit tired, in spite of his late hours.

"You're a sly young fox, Al," Mr. Edison said with a laugh. "I see through your tricks now, though. You bring me the newspapers the way you used to. And I'll let you stay up every night until half-past twelve to practice on your telegraph. Is it a bargain?"

"It's a bargain!" Al agreed, grinning broadly. "I'll run back to Jim's and fetch to-day's papers right now." And he was off for Jim's house in an instant.

When he came back with the papers, he was whistling cheerfully. Not only had he found a way to get more time to learn telegraphy. He had also figured out a scheme which would give him more time to do experiments.

That very day he had asked Conductor Stephenson if he might set up his laboratory in one corner of the baggage car. And Conductor Stephenson had said "yes."

With Mike's help, Al moved his laboratory equipment into the baggage car the following morning. Soon he had put up shelves to hold his test tubes and bottles. And each day, as the train rattled along between stations, he studied and worked out experiments.

It was a busy life the boy was leading. But, now and then, he paid another boy to sell papers for him on the train so that he could take a holiday.

One clear, crisp morning in September, Al stood in the kitchen, watching Hannah wrap

As the train rattled along, he worked out experiments

up chicken sandwiches, hard-boiled eggs, and cookies.

"Are you sure there's enough for Mike and Jim and Sam, too?" he asked anxiously.

"There's enough for a whole army!" Hannah declared. "What are you going to do in Sarnia after you get through looking at the Prince?"

Al shrugged his shoulders. "Just have a good time," he said. And he went outside to help Mike finish his chores. Half an hour later, he and Mike, Sam, and Jim were on the ferry, riding across the river to Sarnia.

The little boat was crowded. Many Port Huron people were crossing to the Canadian shore. For Prince Albert Edward of England was making a trip through Canada. He was stopping in Sarnia that day. And great preparations had been made to welcome him.

By the time the boys reached the little town, the streets were filled with men, women, and children. All eager to see a real live prince. And all making their way to the grandstand, where the Mayor of Sarnia was waiting to greet the man who would some day be the King of England.

"Do you think he'll wear his crown?" Jim asked, as the boys walked up the street from the ferry.

Al didn't hear the question. But Sam said, "Sure he will. It will be all spangled with jewels. And he'll have an ermine cloak, and—"

"Cracky!" Al exclaimed. "Look at that red carpet right down the middle of the street for the Prince to walk on. And the flags everywhere! And all those big arches, covered with flowers. I'll bet—"

Mike grabbed his arm. "The band's beginning to play," he said excitedly. "Maybe he's coming! Let's hurry!"

And hurry they did. But the band was only playing to amuse the crowd. And there was no sign of the Prince. There was other sights to see, however.

A group of Indian chiefs in fine, feathered headdresses had gathered solemnly near the grandstand. Canadian soldiers in bright red uniforms walked up and down, keeping sharp eyes on everyone. The Mayor of Sarnia, in his long black coat, hurried back and forth, giving last-minute directions.

Still the Prince did not come. But the crowd was not impatient. For the sky was blue. The sun was warm. The band kept on playing jolly tunes. And everyone was having a good time.

At last Al and the three other boys decided to eat their lunch. Sitting on the grass, they devoured the food they had brought.

Suddenly, just as Al was finishing his last cookie, there was a cry of "Here he comes!" And the band struck up a solemn tune that sounded like a hymn.

Jumping to his feet, Al peered through the crowd at the carriages which were approaching. Carriages which were drawn by gaily decorated horses and filled with important-looking men.

A hush fell over the crowd as the carriages drew near. Three men stepped from the first carriage. And one—a tall, fine-looking man in a splendid uniform—walked up the steps of the grandstand. The Mayor met him with his hand outstretched.

Al smiled. This man wore no crown. But

he was handsome and strong, just as a prince should be.

"Hurrah!" Al shouted. "Hurrah for the Prince of—"

"Stop your yelling!" exclaimed a red-headed Sarnia boy who was standing beside him. "That's not the Prince! The young man behind him is the Prince."

"That little fellow!" Al exclaimed, staring in amazement at a pale young man in a frock coat, who was just mounting the steps. "Shucks! He's nothing much to look at. He's just a—"

The rest of his sentence was drowned in the cheering of the crowd, as the Prince stepped to the platform. Al promptly forgot what he had just said. But the Canadian boy did not.

By the time the ceremonies were ended, he had gathered five other Sarnia boys around him. And when the crowd broke up Al, Jim, Mike, and Sam found themselves surrounded.

With his fists clenched, the redheaded boy walked toward Al.

"Come on, you young pup!" he cried.

"You're not in the United States now. You're in Canada. What was that you said about our Prince?"

Al grinned and squared his shoulders. He was ready for a fight, if this boy wanted one. He began rolling up his sleeves.

"I said," he declared slowly, "that the Prince wasn't much to look at and—"

With one accord, all the Canadian boys jumped on Al, pummeling him with their fists, kicking, and shouting. At once Jim, Mike, and Sam leaped into the battle. But they didn't stand a chance against the Canadians, and Al was the first to see it.

"Run for it!" he shouted. And, ducking under the arm of the redheaded boy, he raced down the street toward the river. The other boys from Port Huron followed him, while the Sarnia boys stood and jeered.

Al and his friends boarded the ferry hastily. Their clothes were torn. Their faces were bruised. Mike was nursing a sore shin. Sam's nose was swelling and his shirt was covered with blood. Jim had a black eye. And so did Al.

[83]

"I never heard of such foolishness," Mrs. Edison declared, as she laid a piece of raw beefsteak over Al's eye when he reached home.

"That was a rude remark in the first place. And you had no business repeating it."

Al winced as she fastened the raw meat securely in place.

"It would have been a good fight if they hadn't all jumped on me at once," he said. "I hope I'll never have to hear anything more about that old prince again!"

But he did! Many years later, after Prince Albert Edward had become the King of England, he sent a letter to Mr. Thomas Alva Edison. And with it, he sent Edison a beautiful medal of gold.

CHAPTER EIGHT

Bad News

It WAS a cloudless summer night. There was no moon, but the stars shone brightly. The tall pine trees on either side of the road stood black and motionless against the sky.

Al whistled softly as he and Mike walked toward home together from Port Huron. He had only three newspapers under his arm, and his pocket was filled with coins.

"We could have sold twenty more papers tonight, if we'd had them," he said gaily. "People were grabbing for them so fast I had to hold tight to these I was keeping for Father. If this war gets any worse—"

"Listen!" Mike commanded. "Hear that

[*86*]

bugle over at the Fort? Does that remind you of anything?"

He burst out laughing and so did Al.

The military reservation of Fort Gratiot was right across the road from the Edisons' house. Many soldiers were being trained there, to fight on the Northern side in the dreaded Civil War which had broken out at last.

For the past two nights, Al and Mike had played a trick on some of those soldiers.

"Let's hide in the same place and try it again tonight!" Al said eagerly, as the boys approached the reservation.

"I will, if you will," Mike agreed. "It makes me laugh every time I think about it. The way that funny fat corporal comes running all the way from the barracks to see why the sentry wants him—"

"And the sentry doesn't want him at all," Al added with a chuckle. "Jiminy, that corporal gets mad! You'd think the poor loony would catch on after the first time, wouldn't you?"

"Maybe he will tonight," Mike warned.

[*87*]

"We'll have to be ready to run like blazes if he does. It will be the guardhouse for us, if they catch us."

He pushed open the Edisons' front gate as he spoke. The boys started up the path.

"You wait in the back yard while I take Father his papers," Al said. And he ran up the front steps, two at a time.

He found his father reading aloud in the back parlor, and his mother knitting a long gray sock. For several minutes he and his parents talked together.

"Mike and I are going out awhile, Mother," Al said at last. "I'll eat my supper when I come back, if you'll just leave it on the table."

Mrs. Edison looked at her son doubtfully. She was about to tell him that he must eat his supper before he went out again. But she changed her mind.

After all, Al was fourteen now. He had been earning his own living for nearly two years.

"And he's growing up, even if he does forget to wash behind his ears and put on a clean shirt when he needs it," she thought. "I must

[88]

stop treating him as if he were still a child."

"All right," she said aloud. "I'll leave your supper for you. Don't stay out late, Al. Your father and I are going to bed very soon."

Al smiled. "I'll take care not to wake you when I come in," he promised. And he left the room.

With a puzzled frown, Mrs. Edison turned to her husband.

"Have you noticed anything strange about Al, lately?" she asked. "He stares right at you when he knows you're speaking to him. And if he isn't looking at you, he doesn't seem to hear half you say. Do you think there's something wrong with his ears, Sam?"

Mr. Edison laughed. "There's nothing wrong with any part of that boy!" he declared, reaching for a newspaper. "You fuss over him just like a hen with one chicken."

Unfolding the paper, he began to read the headlines. Meanwhile, Al and Mike were making their way quietly toward the big clumps of bushes at one corner of the Fort Gratiot parade ground.

[89]

Looking around quickly to see that no one was watching them, they crawled into the thickest clump. There they crouched in silence for a long time, waiting and watching.

At the far side of the parade ground, half a mile away, was the Fort, where the soldiers were sleeping in their barracks. The night was very still, except for the humming of insects and the sighing of a little breeze through the pine trees.

At last Mike heard the sound of slow, regular footsteps. He put a hand on Al's knee to warn him that a sentry was approaching.

The footsteps came nearer. A tall soldier with a long gun over his shoulder marched past the bushes. He was so close that the boys could almost touch him.

"We'll wait till he gets out of sight," Al whispered, after the sentry had marched on for some distance. "I wonder if he'll pass the call along again tonight like—"

"Corporal of the Guard!" Mike shouted very loudly. "Corporal of the Guard, Number One!"

He was so close that the boys could almost touch him

Breathlessly the boys waited for the call to be passed on. And for the fat corporal to come running from the Fort. But the call was not repeated. No one came rushing out of the barracks.

"This is bad!" Al whispered. "Maybe they're laying for us, this time. We'd better get out of here!"

He crawled quietly from the clump of bushes to the road. Scrambling to his feet, he looked around. There was no one in sight.

"Hurry up, Mike!" he said softly. But he had hardly spoken when there was a hoarse yell from the bushes. Then Mike's voice rang out.

"They've caught me, Al! Run for it! Run!"

Suddenly the bushes seemed alive with soldiers. Al couldn't help Mike now, and he knew it. He sped down the road. Leaping the Edisons' fence, he tore around the house and into the cellar.

It was dark as pitch. But he knew the cellar so well that he needed no light. He felt his way to the potato barrels, for he remembered that one of them was nearly empty. Lifting it quickly, he poured the potatoes from it into another barrel. Then he turned it upside down.

There was no time to lose! Already he could hear men shouting angrily in the yard, and pounding on the back door. Tipping up the barrel, he crawled under it hastily. With his breath coming hard and his heart thudding, he waited to see what would happen next.

Soon, through a crack in the barrel, he saw his father come downstairs from the kitchen. Mr. Edison's nightcap was askew, and he was carrying a candle. The fat corporal and two other soldiers were behind him. They also had candles. Holding them high, they poked around in every corner of the cellar.

"I certainly saw that boy run in here!" the corporal said at last. "I don't see how he could get out! Is there a secret hiding place in here, mister?"

"No, Corporal," replied Mr. Edison. "There is not!"

"It's extraordinary!" said the corporal

[*93*]

gruffly. "Most extraordinary! If I could just lay my hands on the young rascal, I'd throw him in the guardhouse with that other boy!"

"Well, you can see there's no one here," boomed Mr. Edison. "So if you men will get on your way—"

"Yes, sir," said the corporal. "Sorry to have disturbed you."

He stamped up the stairs. Mr. Edison and the soldiers followed him, and Al sighed with relief. For a long time, however, he did not dare to move from his hiding place. Finally he lifted the barrel cautiously and crept out from under it.

His legs and arms were cramped and aching. He had been nearly suffocated by the smell of the rotten potatoes which had clung to the sides of the barrel. And he wondered unhappily what was happening to Mike in the guardhouse.

Feeling his way to the stairs, he crept up to the kitchen. The house was dark and quiet. Al stole up to his room and shut the door.

He did not fall asleep for several hours. And

he wakened quickly when his father strode into his room early the next morning. Mr. Edison had a switch in his hand.

"Mike's just come home," he said. "The soldiers let him out fifteen minutes ago. I didn't know until now that you were the boy they were looking for in the cellar last night. Get up."

"What are you going to do?" Al asked, staring at his father in amazement.

"Whip you," replied Mr. Edison. "I've never done this before. And I hope I'll never have to do it again, but—"

"We didn't mean anything bad!" Al exclaimed quickly. "It was all in fun. I—"

His father broke in sternly. "There's nothing funny about plaguing soldiers who are getting ready to go to war. Get up."

"Yes, sir," Al said soberly. He climbed out of bed and gritted his teeth.

Mr. Edison's arm was strong. His switch left stinging red marks on Al's bare legs. But the boy didn't move until the whipping was over. Then he turned to his washstand and began to pour some water into the blue china bowl.

"Will you remember now that war is a serious business?" his father asked in a low tone.

Al did not reply.

"Al!" exclaimed Mr. Edison sharply. "Answer my question!"

Al turned around. "I'm sorry. I—I didn't hear you," he said.

His father looked at him anxiously. Suddenly he remembered what Mrs. Edison had said to him about Al the night before.

"Is that the truth, son?" he asked. "Didn't you really hear me?"

Al shook his head. The tears, which he had held back when his father had whipped him, now rushed to his eyes. He brushed them away hastily.

"I don't hear lots of things that people say to me any more," he replied, trying to smile.

For a moment Mr. Edison did not speak. When he did, his face was grave.

"Al," he said, "I want you to ask Jim to sell your papers for you on the train today. Then you and your mother are going over to Dr.

Marshall's. He'll find out what's wrong, right away."

So Jim took over Al's job for the day. That afternoon Al and his mother went to see Dr.

Marshall. The doctor examined the boy long and carefully.

"Have you ever had an accident to your ears?" he asked when he had finished.

"Yes, sir," Al said. And he told Dr. Marshall of the time when Bill, the brakeman, had lifted him by the ears to the train platform at Fraser. The doctor turned soberly to Mrs. Edison.

"It's a wonder your son hears as well as he does," he declared. "I'm afraid there's nothing anyone can do to help him. And his deafness will grow worse as he grows older."

"Does Dr. Marshall mean that some day I won't be able to hear anything at all?" Al asked, as he and his mother started home.

Mrs. Edison nodded. "You should have told me about that accident long ago, Al," she said.

She looked so sad that Al smiled at her quickly. "I knew it would just worry you," he remarked cheerfully. "And being deaf is nothing to fret about, Mother. It won't be so bad. I can read or study when people are jabbering all around me, and—"

He stopped speaking. Suddenly he didn't feel nearly as cheerful as he was trying to sound. It would be very strange to live in a world where one heard nothing at all!

"But that won't happen for a long time," he

told himself. "And I've got so many things to do that I won't have a minute to think about it."

Squaring his shoulders, he turned to his mother. And he began to tell her of an idea which had been in his mind for several days.

"If I can buy the things I need and learn to use them, I'll have a surprise for Father, all right," he said. "You won't say anything about it to him, will you?"

"Not a word," his mother promised, smiling and patting his arm. And she kept that promise, though many days passed before Al was ready with his surprise.

CHAPTER NINE

Al Saves a Life

A L PUT a piece of wood into the big stove in the back parlor. He glanced impatiently at the clock on the mantel. Then he spoke to his mother, who sat near the lamp, mending one of his nightshirts.

"Here comes Father at last!" he exclaimed. Picking up a book, he sat down hastily and pretended to read. When Mr. Edison walked in, Al only looked up long enough to say, "Hello." But out of the corner of his eye, he watched his father eagerly.

Mr. Edison greeted his wife and son.

"Did anything special happen today?" he asked, as he sat down in his big chair.

Al grinned and winked at his mother. "No, nothing special," he said quietly.

[*100*]

Mr. Edison reached for the little pile of newspapers which Al had brought home as usual. He eyed the headlines of the first paper and laid it aside. Then he picked up the second newspaper. It was smaller than the others.

"Hey!" he exclaimed. "What's this? A new paper?"

"Yes," Al answered, winking again at his mother. "It's going to be printed once a week. What do you think of it?"

His eyes danced as he waited for his father's reply. Mr. Edison looked slowly down one column of the paper and nodded his head. "It seems to be pretty good," he said. "The editor is mighty smart, printing local news like this. Too bad he can't spell better!"

"What's the matter with my spelling?" Al asked quickly.

"*Your* spelling!" his father exclaimed. "Jehoshaphat, Al! Did you write this stuff?"

Al got to his feet, grinning from ear to ear. He leaned over his father's shoulder and pointed proudly to the words:

THE WEEKLY HERALD
Published by A. Edison

Mr. Edison stared at them as though he couldn't believe his eyes. "Well, I'll be jiggered!" he said with a chuckle. "Who printed this paper for you?"

"I did it myself," Al replied, still grinning broadly. "I bought an old hand press and everything else I needed, in Detroit, about a month ago. Conductor Stephenson let me put the press in the baggage car right next to my laboratory and—"

"And you printed this paper on a *moving* train?" his father asked in amazement. "I never heard of such a thing!"

"I had to do a lot of experimenting with the type," Al declared. "It's still not set quite right. That line there is crooked, you see, and—"

"But you've done a mighty good job!" his father broke in. "Here, Nancy, just take a look at this. I'll bet it's the first newspaper in all the world to be printed on a train."

Mrs. Edison smiled. "I've seen the paper," she said proudly. "Al told me some time ago that he was planning to surprise you with it. He's sold every copy he's printed, Sam, except that one."

"And for three cents a copy!" Al added gleefully. "Regular subscribers will get it for eight cents a month, though. Do you want to subscribe, Father?"

"Indeed I do," Mr. Edison replied promptly. "How many copies do you plan to print each week?"

Al scratched his nose. "I guess a hundred will be all that I can sell," he said. But his guess was wrong.

Al filled his little newspaper full of jokes, and rhymes, and stories about people who lived in the towns between Port Huron and Detroit. He printed war news in it, too. Soon

[103]

the *Weekly Herald* had become so popular that he was selling from four to five hundred copies every week.

His regular newspaper and magazine business was very good. He was making all the money he needed to buy books and chemicals for his experiments. Day after day, he was busy from morning until night.

Yet he found time to go ice-skating on moonlit nights that winter with Mike and the other boys. And when summer came, he often swam with them in the cool waters of the river.

He was longing for a swim one hot August morning, when his train pulled in at Mt. Clemens. It was here that the train for Detroit stopped each day to pick up loaded freight cars. Sometimes it took the train crew nearly half an hour to shunt these cars back and forth.

Al sold several newspapers to people on the depot platform. Then he went into the station to talk to his good friend, Mr. Mackenzie.

Mr. Mackenzie was busy, however, sending a telegraph message. Al watched him for a moment, then wandered outside again. The Mackenzies lived in rooms which were connected

with the depot, and he could see Mrs. Mackenzie hanging out clothes in the yard.

For a moment he thought of going to talk to
her. But he changed his mind when he remembered what a soft voice she had.

"I hate to keep asking her to say things
twice," he told himself. Suddenly he smiled.

"Hi, Jimmy!" he called. And he waved to
tiny Jimmy Mackenzie, who was playing with
some pebbles on the platform near the freight
house.

Jimmy waved back and went on playing. Al
leaned against the depot wall. Idly he watched
a locomotive moving down the side track, to
pick up a freight car loaded with stone.

The engine pulled the freight car to the
main track. Then Bill, the brakeman, uncou-
pled the car.

"All right!" he shouted to the engineer.
"Give her a shove, Tim!" And he jumped out
of the way.

Tim backed the engine against the freight
car with a bang. The heavily loaded car started
to roll down the main track toward the rest of
the train. At that very moment little Jimmy

[*105*]

ran onto the track to gather more pebbles.

"The baby!" a woman on the platform screamed. "The baby! Look out!"

Al swung around at the cry. Dropping his papers, he dashed for the child. He grabbed Jimmy around the waist. Quickly he threw him to the gravel embankment on the other side of the track. At that instant he lost his balance and fell headlong into the same embankment, just as the car rolled by.

For a moment Al lay still. Then, breathing heavily, he rolled over and sat up. Bill and several other men were now running across the track. Mrs. Mackenzie was flying from the yard. And Mr. Mackenzie was hurrying from the depot.

Bill reached the spot first. He picked Jimmy up and handed him to his mother. The child was crying lustily. Though his face and hands had been cut by sharp pieces of gravel, he was not badly hurt.

Al's face and hands had been cut, too.

"But I'm all in one piece," he announced, rather shakily, as he got to his feet.

He fell headlong into the same embankment,
just as the car rolled by

"It's a lucky thing you didn't lose your leg!" Bill exclaimed, eyeing him anxiously. "The wheel of that car scraped right against the heel of your boot. I saw it, and—"

"I felt it," Al said with a little laugh. "How's Jimmy?"

"Alive, thanks to you, Al," Mr. Mackenzie declared. "That was quick thinking, boy. One second more and—"

"And we'd have lost our little son," Mrs. Mackenzie put in, with tears streaming down her face. "There's no way we can thank you, Al. No way, at all."

Al smiled and said nothing, for he hadn't heard a word she had spoken. Just then Bill touched him on the arm.

"Better get to Mackenzies' kitchen and wash the blood off your face before the train leaves," he said. "If you don't, you'll scare off your customers."

Al nodded and started for the kitchen. Mr. Mackenzie followed him, with one arm around his wife, and Jimmy still sobbing against his shoulder.

Fifteen minutes later, Al's face and hands were clean, though blood still oozed from a long cut on his cheek. Brushing off his clothes, he went into the depot.

Someone had gathered up his newspapers and laid them on a bench. As Al picked them up, Mr. Mackenzie stepped out from the office.

"Al," he said earnestly, "Mary's right. There's no way we can thank you for saving Jimmy, but—"

"Shucks, I don't want any thanks," Al broke in, looking very uncomfortable. "Jimmy's my friend, and—"

"But I want to do something to reward you, anyway," Mr. Mackenzie went on. "I know you're interested in telegraphy. Would you like to learn to be a railway telegraph operator?"

"You bet I would," Al replied eagerly.

"All right, I'll teach you," declared Mr. Mackenzie with a smile. "You hire a boy to sell your papers between here and Detroit. Then you can stop off every day and work with me until the train gets back. When you've learned

[*109*]

all that I can show you, you'll be ready to get a regular railway job."

"Can we start working together tomorrow?"

Al asked, shifting his papers from one arm to the other.

"We can," Mr. Mackenzie replied. And they did.

Al already knew the Morse code. But he had a great deal to learn before he could become a railroad telegraph operator.

Railroad telegraphers used a special code of train signals. They were responsible for wiring to stations along the line, telling when trains would arrive. They were also responsible for warning other operators about floods, broken rails, and accidents. In most depots, they sold tickets and gave out information to passengers, too.

Al enjoyed the work with Mr. Mackenzie and learned quickly. Meanwhile he managed to carry on his newspaper business with the help of Jim Clancy and other boys he had hired. And to write and print the *Weekly Herald*. And to work out experiments in his laboratory, while the train was running between Mt. Clemens and Port Huron.

Never had the weeks passed so swiftly. September came and faded into October almost before he knew it. The trees shed their leaves. November arrived, and all was going well with young Al Edison. But trouble was on the way!

CHAPTER TEN

Great Changes for Al

JIM CLANCY sat on a trunk in the baggage car, whistling softly as he watched Al fill a test tube with a greenish liquid.

"You'd better take the candy and fruit through the train once more," Al remarked, without looking up. "We'll be pulling into Smith's Creek pretty soon."

Jim stood up and reached for his basket. "I'll give it a try," he said. "But I don't think we'll sell another thing tonight, Al. The passengers are all mad because the train's so late, and Conductor Stephenson snaps my head off every time I go past him. What's the matter with that old buzzard, anyway?"

Al shrugged his shoulders. "Don't know," he replied. "He's been cross as a bear with a sore head, lately. Maybe he's got a toothache."

He set the test tube carefully in the rack on his laboratory table. Pulling a notebook toward him, he began to write down the results of his experiment. With the basket over his arm, Jim left the swaying baggage car.

Al closed his notebook a moment later. Then he picked up a jar full of water. There was a stick of white phosphorus in the water. He held the jar up and eyed the phosphorus closely.

Suddenly the train lurched. The jar slipped from Al's hand. The stick of phosphorus slid out. Even before it hit the floor, it burst into flames, sending up a great cloud of white smoke.

Al was terrified. He forgot the buckets of sand and water which were carried in the car, for use in case of fire. Yanking off his jacket, he tried to beat out the flames with it. But the fire spread. The smoke grew thicker.

In a panic, the boy yelled for help. At that

instant Conductor Stephenson came rushing into the baggage car.

"Hey, what's all this smoke?" he cried excitedly. "Get out of my way, you idiot!"

Shoving Al aside, he snatched up a bucket of sand and dumped it on the flames. Then he

grabbed a pail of water and emptied that on the fire, too.

Smoking and sizzling, the flames died down. The fire went out, leaving a mess of sand and water and a charred hole in the floor of the car.

Furiously the conductor turned on Al.

[114]

"All right!" he exclaimed, his face red with rage. "You've nearly set the train on fire! What are you going to do about it?"

"I—I'm sorry," Al stammered. "I'll pay for the damage and—"

"Pay for it!" roared Conductor Stephenson. "You won't get a chance to pay for it, you crazy fool! I'm putting you off this train right now! And you'll never ride on it again!"

Picking the rack of test tubes from the table, he thrust it at Al, just as the train jerked to a stop at Smith's Creek.

"Get off now, before I throw you off," he commanded. "I'm sick and tired of having this car used as a laboratory, and a printing office, and a library, and—get off!"

He swung Al around, grabbed him by the shoulders, and pushed him toward the door. Twisting and turning, Al tried to break away.

"My things!" he cried in dismay. "My printing press and—"

"You'll get them," shouted the angry conductor. And he gave the boy another push.

Al jumped, landing safely in front of the

[*115*]

dimly lighted depot. Test tubes popped out of the rack which he was holding and broke when they fell. Before he could turn around, his

notebook, his coat, and his cap went sailing past his ears.

When the train pulled away from the depot five minutes later, all his laboratory equipment had been dumped out on the platform. So had his printing press and type.

It was after eleven o'clock when young Al Edison reached home that night. Mrs. Edison heard him come up the front steps. Both she and her husband hurried into the hall to meet him. They looked at him anxiously as he opened the door.

"Jim stopped in a little while ago and told us what happened," Mr. Edison said. "Did you get hurt when Stephenson threw you off the train?"

Al shook his head and hung up his coat and cap. "Not a bit," he replied with a weary grin. "But I had to walk ten miles home from Smith's Creek, and I'm hungry enough to eat a whole cow."

"You come right to the kitchen then," his mother said. "Hannah has a good hot supper waiting for you. And you can tell us the whole story while you eat."

So Al sat down at the kitchen table. Between bites of roast pork and crisp fried potatoes, he told his story of the fire on the train. Hannah stood by the stove listening, while she waited for the coffee to boil.

"Do you mean that old ape, Stephenson,

threw *all* your stuff out of the car?" she asked angrily.

Al nodded. "Some things broke to smithereens, but I saved a lot," he said, reaching for a piece of pumpkin pie. "I've left everything at Smith's Creek with the ticket agent. Tomorrow I'll take the horse and cart, and go and fetch it."

"But what about your newspaper and magazine business, Al?" his father asked. "You worked hard to build that up. I hate to see you lose it."

"I hate to lose it," Al replied soberly. "But there's no use crying over spilt milk. Stephenson will never let me work on his train again and I don't blame him. I'm glad I've saved some money."

"What are you planning to do with it?" his father asked.

"Get my press mended," Al replied, pouring cream into the coffee which Hannah had set before him. "Then I can print my paper here at home, and I'll set up another laboratory down cellar, and—"

"Not in the cellar," Mrs. Edison declared firmly. "You can put your laboratory in the attic this time, Al. We'd rather have you blow the roof off, than have you blow up the whole house."

Al laughed. "I won't blow up the house," he promised. And, picking up his fork, he took a large mouthful of pie.

Within a week he had set up a laboratory and a printing press in the attic. He was also working hard again at his telegraphy. Sometimes he went to Mt. Clemens to study with Mr. Mackenzie. At other times he studied alone. He learned quickly. And when the telegraph operator in Port Huron left to join the Army, Al was given his job.

The Port Huron telegraph office was in Walker's Jewelry Store in the center of town. Al often stayed at the store all night so that he could practice taking down the news reports which came over the wire after midnight. These reports came in so rapidly that this was very difficult work.

"Only the best telegraphers can do it," Al

told Jim Clancy one night, when Jim stopped in at the store for a visit. "I'm getting my speed up, but I still have lots to learn."

"You'll learn it all right," Jim said. He spoke loudly so that Al could hear him. And he glanced at his friend admiringly. "I never knew any fellow who worked as hard as you do."

Al grinned. "It isn't work when you're doing something you like," he declared. "My deafness helps me, too, Jim. I can keep my mind on what I'm doing, no matter how much noise is going on around me. Yet I can hear my telegraph instrument as clear as a bell."

"How does that happen?" Jim asked curiously.

"Don't know," Al replied, running his fingers through his untidy brown hair. "I'm just plain lucky, I guess. Anyway, I mean to stick to telegraphy. I'm going to be a railway operator soon."

"Soon!" Jim repeated with a laugh. "Now you're talking big! You know you ain't old enough yet to land a railway job."

"I'm going to try for one, anyhow," Al said. And he did.

On a fine day in February he burst into the Edisons' house with his face beaming. Mrs. Edison was upstairs, sewing. But she hurried down when she heard Al's voice in the kitchen.

"What are you doing home at this time of day?" she asked. "Is anything wrong?"

Al tried to look very sober. "Well," he said slowly. "I—I've quit my job at Walker's."

"Oh, Al!" his mother exclaimed sadly. "I was afraid Mr. Walker would put you out. I told you not to take any chemicals down to his store. You can't spend time doing experiments, when you're supposed to—"

"But I've got a better job!" Al cried joyfully. He caught his mother around her shoulders and hugged her hard. "I've got a job with the Grand Trunk Railroad!" he said as he let her go. "I'm going to be the night telegraph operator in Stratford."

Mrs. Edison laughed. "You crazy boy!" she exclaimed. "Worrying me like that! Where's Stratford?"

"Seventy-five miles east of here," Al replied, taking a handful of cookies from the big cookie jar. "I have to leave tomorrow. Will you and Hannah get my clothes together while I fetch my stuff from Walker's?"

"Seventy-five miles is a long way off, Al," Mrs. Edison said doubtfully. "I—I don't want you living so far away from home."

Al stared at her in amazement. "But I'm nearly seventeen!" he cried. "I'm a man now, Mother."

Hannah sniffed. "And you're stuffing yourself with cookies like you was seven!" she exclaimed. "I'd better start ironing his shirts right away, hadn't I, Mrs. Edison?"

Mrs. Edison nodded. She had hoped that Al would be content to stay in Port Huron for a long, long time. But she knew that when he had made up his mind to do something, there was little that anyone could do to stop him.

"Yes, Hannah," she said. "Iron his shirts. And then please clean the spots off the suit he wears on Sundays. Al, you go to the attic and bring down the little leather trunk. Put it in your room, and we'll pack it there tonight."

Whistling merrily, Al ran up to the attic and brought down the trunk. Then he set off for his father's store to tell Mr. Edison the exciting news.

That night Al filled his trunk so full of science books that his mother declared he had left no room for clothes. But she and Hannah managed to pack everything at last. And early the next morning young Al Edison set out for Stratford to take his first job away from home.

CHAPTER ELEVEN

Hard Times and Good Luck

IT WAS a beautiful September day, and the sun shone brightly on the city of New York. Young Mr. Thomas Edison stood on the corner of a busy street, watching for a chance to cross.

Wagons and carriages rattled past him over the bumpy cobblestones. Two horsecars rolled by, with bells clanging noisily. An omnibus stopped on the opposite corner to pick up passengers. And a blue-coated policeman in a tall helmet whistled shrilly. Suddenly the traffic halted.

Ducking under the nose of a huge dray horse, young Edison hurried across the street

[*124*]

and turned down Broadway. Opening the door of a Western Union Telegraph office, he stepped inside.

The operator behind the high counter looked up quickly. When he saw Al Edison, he got to his feet.

"Sorry, Edison," he said, leaning over the counter. "I've no job for you yet. Have you tried the other telegraph offices?"

Al nodded and shoved his shabby straw hat to the back of his head. He was tired and hungry and discouraged. In one pocket of his worn blue trousers he had forty-two cents. The other pocket was empty.

"What's the matter with New York, anyway?" he asked impatiently. "I've been able to get work all over the country since I left home five years ago—in Louisville, in Indianapolis, in Cincinnati, in Boston, in half a dozen other places! But I've been in New York three days now, and—"

"Too many people want to work in New York," the operator broke in. "That's why it's so hard to get a job here. Say, are you the Edi-

[125]

son I read about in the *Telegrapher?* The fellow who invented a way to send two messages in opposite directions over one wire at the same time?"

"Yes," Al replied, brightening up. "I've been working on other inventions, too. I haven't had much luck selling them yet. But I mean to go on trying, once I get a job."

The operator glanced at him curiously. "Have you found a place to stay?" he asked.

Young Edison nodded. "Over at the Gold Indicator Company," he replied. "I've a friend there named Frank Pope and he's fixed it up so that I can sleep on the floor in the cellar. Well, I'll be on my way now. See you tomorrow, maybe."

Turning on his heel, Al left the telegraph office. For a moment he stood on the sidewalk, wondering if he dared to step into the restaurant next door, for a cup of coffee and a piece of pie.

In the years since he had left home, he had earned good wages. But he had spent most of his money on books and chemicals. And on materials for his inventions. The forty-two cents in his pocket was all the money he had in the world.

"I'd better not spend another cent of it until I have to," he thought wearily. "Guess I'll go back to the Gold Indicator Company and give my feet a rest."

Rounding a corner, he made his way to the

building where the Gold Indicator Company had its headquarters.

This company sent out information about the price of gold to three hundred business firms near by. The information was sent over private telegraph wires by a transmitter. Since the price of gold changed often, it was important that the transmitter should work well at all times.

Al Edison had already spent several hours studying the machinery in this transmitter. He knew just how it was put together and what every part was for. Yet he still liked to see the big transmitter at work. So he sat down in the office to watch it.

Except for the whirring of the wheels in the transmitter, the room was very quiet. Clerks and office boys were going peacefully about their duties. Suddenly, however, there was a loud clatter. With a rattle and a groan, the transmitter came to a stop.

At once the room was in confusion. Engineers and mechanics came running from the basement. Clerks stopped their work. Mr.

Laws, the head of the company, rushed from his private office.

Messenger boys from near-by business offices burst into the room. Yelling that the wires were broken. Shouting that the indicators in their bosses' offices were not working. Everyone crowded excitedly around the big transmitter.

Hastily the mechanics and the engineers tried to start the machinery again. But they couldn't, and they didn't know why. Meanwhile Al Edison was examining it quietly. His sharp eyes soon spotted what was wrong. Quickly he turned to Mr. Laws.

"I know what's causing the trouble, sir," he said. "I think I can fix it."

"Then fix it!" Mr. Laws cried hastily. "Fix it, and don't stand there wasting time."

"Yes, sir," young Edison replied, and he took off his shabby coat. Rolling up his shirtsleeves, he promptly went to work. Soon he had the transmitter running smoothly again. And before long, he found himself sitting in Mr. Laws' private office.

When he came out of that office, Al Edison's face was one big smile. For Mr. Laws had offered him a job.

"He's put me in charge of all the machinery in the building," Al told Frank Pope, as the two men ate dinner that night. "And he's going to pay me three hundred dollars a month! That's a whopping big salary. I'll have to work like blazes to earn it, but—"

"Will you have any time to go on with your inventions?" Frank Pope asked.

Al Edison nodded. "I can do that at night," he declared. And he began to talk eagerly of an invention on which he had been working for many weeks. This invention was a device called a stock ticker.

There were already many stock tickers in use in business offices. But they did not always work well and it was difficult to repair them when they were out of order. Edison was trying to invent a simple stock ticker which could be easily repaired. When his invention was finished many weeks later, he showed it hopefully to a man named Marshall Lefferts.

Mr. Lefferts was the head of a big business firm in New York. He examined Al Edison's stock ticker carefully. It was better than any other stock ticker he had ever seen.

"I should like my company to be the only company in the world with the right to manufacture stock tickers like this one," he thought. And he turned to Al Edison.

"How much do you want for this invention?" he asked.

For a moment young Edison did not reply. He had worked so long and so hard on the invention that he had planned to ask three thousand dollars for it. But suddenly this seemed a very high price. So high that he could not make his tongue say the words. Rumpling his hair, he looked slowly from his model of the stock ticker to Mr. Lefferts.

"What—what do you think the invention's worth?" he blurted out.

"Forty thousand dollars," Mr. Lefferts replied calmly.

Al's heart skipped a beat. He was so taken by surprise that he could not speak.

[*131*]

"How much do you want for this invention?" he asked

Forty thousand dollars! Why, he'd have money enough to buy plenty of material for new inventions. Money enough to rent work-rooms where he could manufacture the things he invented. Money enough to hire men to help him.

He'd have money to send to his mother, who had been ill for many months. Money to help his father, who was growing old. *Forty thousand dollars!* He swallowed hard.

"Thank you, Mr. Lefferts," he said. "I—I think that would be a very fair price."

"Splendid!" exclaimed Mr. Lefferts. "Come back in three days, young man, and I'll give you a check for that amount."

"Yes, sir," Al Edison replied. And, like a man in a dream, he left the office.

That night he wrote to his mother and father to tell them the good news. What excitement there was in Port Huron when that letter arrived! All over town people were talking about Al Edison and his stock ticker.

In the little city of Newark, New Jersey, people were soon talking about Edison, too.

For he had opened workrooms and a laboratory there, at 10 Ward Street. He had hired a number of men to help him. And often the neighbors saw his oil lamps burning long after midnight while he labored over his inventions.

Old Mrs. Mulligan, who lived across the street, was worried about him. She spoke about this one winter evening, as she and two friends visited together in her kitchen.

"It ain't right for that young man to work so hard," she said, shaking her head. "I keep watch of him from behind my window curtain. He don't go out to eat his meals regular. His clothes are a sight, and—"

"He's awful deaf!" Mrs. O'Brien broke in. "At least that's what Pat Flaherty told me."

Little Mrs. Schmidt nodded her head. "He's deaf, all right," she agreed. "But it don't seem to bother him any. My son John works for him now, and he says Mr. Edison is the best-natured young fellow he ever knew. Always laughing and full of jokes! And so kind to his men they'd do anything to please him."

Mrs. Mulligan sniffed. "Just the same, he

works too hard," she insisted. "What he needs is a good wife to look after him."

Although Mrs. Mulligan did not know it, Al Edison was already thinking of getting married. He had fallen in love with a pretty girl in Newark named Mary Stilwell. She soon learned to love him. And on Christmas day in the year 1871, they were married.

Mary Edison called her young husband Tom. She thought he was the most wonderful man in the world. It wasn't many years before people all over the country, and even abroad, were thinking much the same thing.

CHAPTER TWELVE

The Wizard of Menlo Park

THE August sun was low in the sky. A gentle breeze stirred the maple trees growing near the Edisons' big house in Menlo Park, New Jersey. And the fragrance of freshly cut grass filled the air.

On the wide lawn in front of the house, Mr. Thomas Edison was playing with his children. Suddenly he bent over, stood on his head, and waved his feet in the air.

Four-year-old Marion Edison shouted with glee. Little Tom stared at his father with wide eyes. Mrs. Edison, who was sitting on the long front porch, laughed aloud.

"Watch out, Tom!" she called to her husband. "Everything will fall out of your pockets!"

Mr. Edison flipped his legs over and stood up, grinning broadly.

"Do it again, Father," Marion shrieked, jumping up and down excitedly. "Do it again!"

Her father shook his head. "Not now," he said with a smile. And picking up little Tom, he swung him to his shoulder.

Marion tugged at her father's arm. "Do another trick," she begged. "Please do another."

Once more Mr. Edison shook his head. "Look," he said, "there's Delia waiting in the doorway to put you to bed. Here, give me your hand."

Catching the little girl by the hand, and holding tightly to Tom, he took both children up the steps. He and Mrs. Edison kissed them good night. And Delia, the nurse, led them away to the cozy nursery on the top floor.

Mr. Edison watched them climb the stairs. Then he pulled a cigar from his pocket and sat down in a chair close to his wife.

[*137*]

Picking up little Tom, he swung him to his shoulder

"I think our Dot and Dash are the smartest youngsters in the United States!" he exclaimed, as he lighted a match.

Mrs. Edison smiled. "Why do you call them by those foolish nicknames?" she asked.

"I don't know," her husband replied with a little chuckle. "Perhaps I do it because it reminds me of the time when I learned the Morse code, back in Port Huron."

He puffed quietly on his cigar for several minutes, thinking about Port Huron. About his mother, who had died several years earlier. And about his father.

"I hope Father will come here soon for another visit," he said aloud. Tossing his half-smoked cigar into the bushes, he got to his feet.

Mrs. Edison glanced at him quickly. "Are you going back to the laboratory to work again tonight?" she asked anxiously.

Her husband nodded. "My mind's just popping with plans for things that I want to invent," he said eagerly. "They are all things that people need, too, Mary.

"Take the talking telephone, for instance.

Sounds come through it so faintly that it's of no use to anyone. I want to invent a mouthpiece that will send voices over the wires so loudly that a person with good ears can hear them across a room. I know there's a way to do this. But I haven't found it yet."

"You'll find it, if anyone can," Mary Edison said, getting to her feet. And she watched her husband proudly, as he strode across the lawn toward his laboratory, which was not far away. She wished that she could understand more about his work.

"I'm afraid Tom thinks I'm very stupid," she told herself, as she turned to go indoors.

But Thomas Edison did not think his wife was stupid at all. There were very few people who could understand all the things he was trying to do. Even his workmen were sometimes bewildered by his ideas. Indeed, it was just a week later that one of his mechanics came to him with his forehead wrinkled in a puzzled frown.

"Here, Mr. Edison," he said, setting a strange-looking machine before the inventor.

"I made this contraption just like you told me to. But I'll be jiggered if I know what it's for."

Thomas Edison's eyes twinkled. "If that machine acts the way I hope it will, Kruesi, it will talk," he announced solemnly.

"Talk!" John Kruesi repeated in surprise. He stared anxiously at Edison. "Do you—do you feel all right, Boss?" he asked. "You don't feel light in the head, maybe, from working too hard? Machines can't—talk."

"This one will, if we're lucky," Edison declared with a laugh. "It will repeat everything I say to it." He turned to a man who was standing near his elbow. "Get me some sheets of tin foil, please, Carman," he said.

"Yes, sir," replied Mr. Carman.

He handed Edison some tin foil. By this time several other workmen had gathered about the table. They watched curiously as the inventor wrapped a piece of the shiny foil around a cylinder on the little machine.

"That thing ain't ever going to work, Boss," one of the men announced. "I'll bet you two dollars that it won't say a word."

[*141*]

"I'll bet you a barrel of apples that it will," Edison replied, trying to sound more sure of this than he felt. He had not spent many hours on this particular invention. But he was just as anxious to have it work as if he had spent months on it.

"All right, boys, I guess we're ready," he said. Slowly and carefully, he began to turn a crank which was attached to the cylinder.

The men watched him intently as he bent over the machine.

"Mary had a little lamb," he shouted at the top of his lungs:

"Its fleece was white as snow.

"And everywhere that Mary went—"

He looked and sounded so funny that some of the workmen burst out laughing. But this did not disturb Mr. Edison.

"The lamb was sure to go," he finished in a loud voice. Then he straightened up. "Now we'll see what happens," he said eagerly. And he moved the cylinder back to the starting point. Then, once more, he began to turn the crank.

"Mary had a little lamb." The words came clearly from the machine.

Kruesi gasped. The rest of the men looked at each other in amazement. But not a word was spoken until the nursery rhyme was finished. Then one of the men broke into a cheer.

"It's him!" another cried excitedly. "It's the Boss's voice, just like he was talking!"

Mr. Edison's face was beaming. He clapped

Kruesi on the back. He gave Carman a poke in the ribs with his elbow.

"It works!" he exclaimed joyfully. "I wasn't sure it would! But, by golly, my talking machine works!"

With fingers that shook a little, he took off the tin foil and laid it carefully to one side. Soon he had fastened another piece around the cylinder.

"Come on, fellows, say something!" he cried.

So they did. All the rest of the day and through most of the night, they talked and sang and shouted at the machine. And a blunt pin scratching on the tin foil made records of their voices as they turned the crank.

Many of the recorded sounds were not perfect, when the machine repeated them. But when Thomas Edison went home at dawn he was whistling like a boy.

"I'll find ways to make that phonograph better and better," he told his wife that day at the dinner table.

"Just think what it means, Mary! I can make

records of the voices of all kinds of people. Actors, statesmen, singers—why, some day, perhaps, I can even make a record of an opera, or a whole orchestra. And people can sit right in their own homes and—"

Mary Edison reached over and touched his arm. "You won't be able to do any of those things unless you take care of yourself, Tom," she said gently. "Now, please eat some dinner."

Her husband smiled. But he was almost too excited to eat. And he had good reason to be. In no time at all the story of his wonderful invention had spread throughout the country and to foreign countries.

Newspapers and magazines printed accounts of the machine that could talk. Day after day, all that winter and spring, hundreds of people flocked to the laboratory in Menlo Park to see and hear the phonograph.

Famous men and women came to have records made of their voices. The President of the United States asked to have the phonograph brought to Washington, so that he might listen to it. Soon the name of Thomas Edison was on millions of tongues.

Meanwhile Edison was trying to find stronger material than tin foil on which he could make records. He was also trying to improve his phonograph. And he had begun again to work on a mouthpiece for the telephone. For he still hoped to make this instrument really useful.

Week after week, he continued to experiment with the mouthpiece. At last good news went out from the laboratory:

"Mr. Edison has invented a carbon transmitter for the mouthpiece of the telephone. It sends voices over the wires clearly and strongly. With the Edison transmitter, a man can whisper in New York and be heard plainly in Philadelphia."

"That Thomas Edison is certainly a wizard!" people exclaimed when this news reached them. "There isn't anything that he can't do."

This talk about Mr. Edison pleased his wife. But she was worried about the long hours which her husband was spending in his laboratory. And she was delighted when he took some time, now and then, to drive the family to Boynton Beach to go bathing.

Marion and little Tom were delighted, too. For they loved to play in the sand and to run from the waves. And to watch their father floating on his back and spouting like a whale.

One day late that summer the Edisons rode home from the beach, all sandy and sunburned. Mrs. Edison sat in the back seat of the carriage, with her new baby, William, in her arms. Little Tom was beside her, sound asleep in Delia's lap. Marion was in the front seat, wide awake, and sitting just as close to her father as she could get.

"Will you be a whale again tomorrow?" she asked, as Mr. Edison lifted her from the carriage when they reached home.

"Perhaps," her father replied, tousling her yellow hair.

But when the next day came, Thomas Edison was far too busy to think about being a whale. He had begun to work on an invention which was to change the homes of people all over the world. And many busy months passed before he went to the beach with his children again.

CHAPTER THIRTEEN

Edison Turns Night into Day

IT WAS nearly twelve o'clock on a cool October night in the year 1879. Every home in Menlo Park was dark. But in the little gray laboratory building on the hill, gaslights were flickering.

In one corner of the upstairs room, Thomas Edison sat with his feet propped on a table, talking with some of his men. Suddenly he swung his feet to the floor.

"Well, that's all, boys," he announced, getting up from his chair. "You fellows build that dynamo the way I've designed it, to give us more electricity, and I'll keep on experimenting with the bulb. I'm going to invent a good electric light if it takes me the rest of my life."

He swung around on his heel and shouted down the stairs. "Hey, Swanson," he called. "We're all hungry. Got any food?"

"Coming up, Mr. Edison," the night watch-man called back. And a moment later he clumped up the stairs with a basket on his arm. It was well filled with ham sandwiches, crackers, cheese, and apples. The men gathered around it and helped themselves.

Biting into a sandwich, Edison strolled over to a little organ at the front of the room. He began to pick out a tune with one finger. Soon the men were all gathered around him, singing lustily.

For some time they sang and joked and laughed together. Then they left to go to their homes. Tall, slim Frank Upton and a black-haired boy named Francis Jehl were the last to leave. At the head of the stairs, Mr. Upton turned to shout good night to Edison.

He changed his mind when he saw the inventor. For Mr. Edison had seated himself in his armchair again. His feet were propped on the table, and he was staring at the wall.

"He's likely to sit there thinking about his light bulb all night," Mr. Upton said to Francis as the two made their way down the dark street. "I never saw such a man. When you figure how long he's been experimenting with that light, you'd think he'd be discouraged."

"Not him," young Francis declared stoutly. "The Boss don't ever get discouraged."

But Thomas Edison *was* discouraged, though he would never let his men know it. Nearly a year had passed since he had decided to invent an electric light which could be used in homes. Nearly a year of hard, steady work, with little to show for it.

Electric arc lights had already been invented by someone else. But they burned out quickly. They blazed so brightly that they hurt the eyes. And they could not safely be used indoors.

Edison intended to invent a better, cheaper light which could be used safely anywhere. He had decided to use a glass bulb for this light. For many months he had been searching for some material to use in the bulb which would glow steadily when an electric current passed through it.

Week after week, he had patiently experimented with loops of horsehair, straw, corn silk, splinters of wood, twine, and countless other things.

"And every material I've tried has blown out, or burned up, or broken when we've turned on the electric current," he thought, as

he slumped down farther in his armchair. "I might try cotton thread again. Last time we used it we hadn't discovered that we had to pump all the air out of the bulb before we turned on the current, and—"

Clasping his hands behind his head, he began to plan how he would prepare cotton thread for use in a vacuum bulb. It was dawn and gray light was creeping through the windows before he stood up.

[*152*]

"I believe I've got it," he said under his breath. "It will be worth a try, anyway. Well, it's too late now to go home, I guess."

Yawning and stretching, he turned off the gas. Then, pushing aside some batteries on his table, he lay down with his head on two books. There he slept soundly until his men returned to work a few hours later.

It was not long after this that Thomas Edison sat at his laboratory table with several skeins of cotton thread before him. Carefully —very carefully—he rolled pieces of this thread in a fine paste made of lampblack. Then he bent them into hairpin shapes and laid them gently in a small clay mold.

"Now we'll bake them," he said to Francis Jehl, who had been helping him. And he put the mold into a small furnace downstairs.

Many hours passed before the mold was removed from the furnace. And many of the delicate black threads were broken before one of them was sealed at last in an airtight glass bulb. Then Thomas Edison turned on the electric current. The bulb glowed brightly.

"That thread's going to pieces just like everything else we've tried," one of the men announced gloomily.

But it didn't! Minute after minute, hour after hour, the bulb with the thread filament burned steadily. With a broad smile on his face, Edison watched it closely. All night and all the next day he sat beside it, waiting to see how long it would burn.

During the day his assistants went about their work as usual. But they stopped often to exclaim over the wonderful light. And when they found the little lamp still burning on the second day, they were so excited that they could not work at all. Shortly after noon the new incandescent lamp suddenly went out.

With one accord everyone in the room glanced at the clock on the wall.

"Forty hours!" John Kruesi shouted. "It's burned forty hours!" Then what cheers went up! And how the rafters rang!

"Forty hours!" Edison exclaimed joyfully, as he broke open the bulb to study the filament. "If I can make a lamp that will burn

All night and all the next day he sat beside it, waiting

forty hours, I can make one that will burn a week."

When he went home, some hours later, his mind was filled with plans for making a better lamp. Plans for lighting homes, offices, factories, and hospitals, with electricity. Plans for lighting whole cities.

Soon newspapers all over the country were printing the story of Edison's wonderful invention. And two months later, on New Year's Eve, more than three thousand people traveled to Menlo Park to see a display of Mr. Edison's lamps.

Men, women, and children came in farm wagons, in fine carriages, and in trains. What a sight met their eyes when they reached the little village that snowy night!

Electric lights shone brightly on both sides of the street which led to the laboratory. Electric lights blazed from the windows of buildings and houses. Electric lights which seemed almost to turn night into day.

"How beautiful!" people exclaimed.

"What a strong, steady light!"

"It's safer than gas or oil or candles. And

I understand it will be cheaper, too, some day."

"It's a miracle! That's what! A miracle!"

Hundreds of the curious throng crowded into the laboratory during the evening to see a bulb that was burning under water. And another which was glowing steadily, after burning for seventeen days. And another on an electric cord, which could be moved around.

Many people looked about eagerly for the inventor of these wonderful lights. But only a few recognized the young man in shabby working clothes, who hurried here and there, watching the humming dynamo and keeping a sharp eye on wires and bulbs.

That night Edison fell into bed so tired that he could hardly move. The next afternoon the house was full of guests who had come to wish the Edisons a happy New Year. When they had gone, Mr. Edison sat down in the library with little Tom on his knee. Marion was playing with a new doll near the big Christmas tree.

The tree was dark, for all the candles had burned out. Edison looked at it thoughtfully. Suddenly he chuckled.

"What are you laughing at?" Marion asked.

Her father cupped his hand to his ear to catch her question. When she came close to him and repeated it, he smiled.

"I won't tell you, Dot," he replied, giving her a hug. "Not till next Christmas! Then I'll have a big surprise for you and Dash."

Sliding Tom to the floor, he went upstairs to speak to his wife, who was rocking the baby, Billy, to sleep. Marion watched her father climb the stairs and shook her head. Next Christmas seemed a long way off.

But it came at last. And when it did, the Edison children jumped up and down with excitement and squealed with delight at the sight of their Christmas tree.

Electric lights shone, bright as stars, on nearly every bough. The colored ornaments gleamed and sparkled in their steady glow.

Marion showed the tree to all the neighbors' children. And she told them proudly that it was the first Christmas tree in all the whole world to be lighted by electric bulbs. She also boasted to the children about the wonderful electric railroad her father was inventing.

How she loved to ride on that railroad when it was finished at last! So did many other people. They came from far and near to see the little electric locomotive. They climbed aboard the open car. Bumping along up hill and down, they rode over the three-mile track which had been built near the Edisons' house.

When Thomas Edison speeded the locomotive up to forty miles an hour, they hung on to their hats. They clutched their seats when he drove the train over high trestles, or took it around sharp curves. And they went home

[159]

talking excitedly about the electric railroad.

Some talked only about what a good time they had had, riding on the first electric railroad in America. Others spoke of the little electric locomotive.

"Perhaps the time will come when big railroads will use engines which are run by electricity," one man said to another. "Is it true that Edison is building a large power plant in New York so that he can light part of the city with his electric lamps?"

"That's right," his friend replied. "He has men there right now, digging ditches so that he can lay his wires underground. Folks living in the neighborhood are scared to death that he'll set the city afire."

But Thomas Edison didn't set the city afire. And one evening in September, after months of hard work, he had everything ready so that he could turn on the lights.

Crowds gathered excitedly in one of the business sections of the city. The inventor pulled a switch in his powerhouse. And the air rang with cheers as electric lights flashed on in homes, in office buildings, and in streets.

That was a great day for New York City and for the whole country. It was a great day for Thomas Edison, too. And happy times followed for all the Edison family.

But they came to an end abruptly when Mrs. Edison was taken ill with typhoid fever. Though her husband watched over her tenderly, he could not help her. Neither could any doctor. On a warm August night, she died.

With a heavy heart, Mr. Edison sent Marion, Tom, and little Bill to live with their Grandmother Stilwell. He rented the house in Menlo Park where he had spent so many pleasant years. He closed the laboratory where he had done such splendid work. And he moved to the house in New York where he had opened offices for the Edison Electric Light Company, some time earlier.

Although he worked even harder than he had in the past, he was lonely and sad. But happier days were ahead. And the name of Thomas Alva Edison was soon to become more famous than ever before.

CHAPTER FOURTEEN

Moving Pictures!

MR. EDISON swallowed the last drop of his breakfast coffee and pushed his chair back from the table. Young Tom looked up quickly from his plate of scrambled eggs.

"Hey, Dad, is anything going on this morning in the Black Maria?" he asked in a loud voice.

His father nodded. "We're going to have a couple of gypsies there with some trained bears," he said, getting to his feet. "If you and Bill want to see some fun, come along with me. I'll meet you outside in ten minutes."

"Whoopee!" Bill cried joyfully. Picking up a spoon, he began to gobble his oatmeal and cream.

Edison laughed and turned to his pretty young wife, who sat at the head of the table. "I'll just run up to the nursery, Mina, and take a peek at Madeleine and Charley before I leave," he told her.

"I'll go with you," Mrs. Edison said with a smile.

Standing up, she linked her arm with her husband's. Together they left the room and started up the broad winding stairs in the hall.

Six years had passed since Thomas Edison had married for the second time. Six busy, happy years. During those years, Edison had moved his family into a splendid home in West Orange, New Jersey. He had built a fine big laboratory. He had been working hard on several inventions. And he and Mrs. Edison had made a trip to Europe, taking Marion along.

What an exciting trip that had been! Wherever the Edisons went in France, Germany, and England, people had gathered to welcome them. They had crowded around Edison in the streets, cheering for the man who had invented the phonograph and electric lamp. They had given magnificent parties for him. They had showered him with gifts.

Edison was thinking of Europe now, as he climbed the broad stairs with his wife. He was thinking also of Marion, who had stayed in Germany to study.

"We should have another letter from Dot soon," he said, as he opened the nursery door. He held out his arms to little Madeleine, who ran to meet him. Lizzie, the nurse, sat by the window, dressing the baby, Charley. She set him on the floor and he toddled toward his mother and father on unsteady legs.

For several minutes Edison played with the children. Then he kissed his wife good-by and went downstairs. Soon he and Tom and Bill were walking through the beautiful park which surrounded their home, toward the laboratory, half a mile away.

It was still early in the morning. But Valley Road, which led to the laboratory buildings, was crowded with men on their way to work. Glass blowers, electricians, mechanics, carpenters, engineers, chemists, photographers, office clerks. And men who did many other kinds of jobs. They streamed through the gate of the high picket fence around the laboratory grounds.

One of the glass blowers had a boy about twelve years old with him. They waited outside the gate until Edison and his sons had reached it. Then the glass blower spoke to the inventor.

"Hey, Mr. Edison," he said, raising his voice, "this is Jack, my sister's boy, from Chicago. He's interested in electricity. Could he come in and go through the laboratory?"

"Sure he could," Edison replied, smiling at the boy from Chicago. "My Tom and Bill can show him around."

Edison turned to the gatekeeper, who stood near by. "Two men are coming here with some trained bears, Nick," he said. "Take them right to the Black Maria when they get here. I'll see you later, boys."

With a wave of his hand, he walked toward the main building, where he had an office. Jack watched him admiringly until he had disappeared. Then he turned suddenly to the Edison boys.

"Hey, what's this Black Maria?" he asked.

"Come and see for yourself," Tom replied. And he led the way to an open space behind the big brick laboratory.

"There it is," he said, pointing to an oddly shaped building with a strange-looking roof. "Doesn't it look like one of those police wagons they call the 'Black Maria'?"

But his question was never answered. For at that moment the strange-looking roof of the

[166]

Black Maria slowly rose in the air! And the whole building began to turn around! Jack stared at it in amazement.

"What in blazes makes it do that?" he cried.

"It's built so that it will swing around and can be turned to face the sun. With the roof up, there's plenty of light for taking moving pictures—"

"For taking *what?*" asked Jack, now very much bewildered. "What's a moving picture?"

"Well," said Bill, "you look at the pictures and you see the people in them move around and—"

"And sometimes they talk, too," Tom broke in.

"Now you're stringing me!" Jack laughed.

"Not a bit," Tom declared soberly. "Dad figured out a way to hook up a phonograph so he can make records of actors talking. One of the men plays the records while you watch the pictures and—hey, look! Here comes Nick with the bears!"

And there was the gatekeeper coming across the yard with two dark-skinned men, each lead-

[*167*]

ing two furry brown bears. Nick took the gypsies and their trained animals into the Black Maria. By this time, several other men had arrived. And Edison himself was walking briskly toward the little moving-picture studio. Taking the boys with him, he went inside.

When the three boys came out some time later, Jack's head was in a whirl. He had laughed with the others at the tricks which the bears had performed on the little stage in the studio. But he had seen something far more wonderful than trained animals.

He had watched the first practical moving-picture camera in all the world, at work. And when the bears had been led away, he had seen something else. For Edison had let the boys watch some motion pictures which had been taken the day before. Pictures in which people moved about, and jumped and danced and ran.

The pictures were short. Indeed, each one lasted only a little over a minute.

"But Dad's working on a camera now that will take longer pictures," Tom explained, as the boys left the Black Maria. "He thinks that some day he'll be able to make moving pictures of a whole opera or a play."

Jack shook his head wonderingly. "No one back in Chicago is ever going to believe me when I tell them about this," he exclaimed. "Your father must be the most famous inventor in the world!"

And he was! Rulers of foreign lands sent him presents. Scientific societies in America and abroad awarded him medals. Indeed, as the years sped by, so many medals were sent to Thomas Edison that he couldn't keep track of them. One of them came with a letter from King Edward VII of England.

How Edison chuckled when he read that letter! It made him think of a day in Sarnia many years earlier. Of a celebration to welcome a prince. Of a fight and a black eye.

One warm July evening he told Madeleine and Charley about that fight. The family had gathered, as usual, in the big second-story parlor. Even the baby, Theodore, was there, playing on the floor near his mother's feet.

Tom was reading a newspaper. Bill was buried in a book. And the others were just finishing a game of parcheesi.

"My mother put beefsteak on my black eye," Mr. Edison said, as he waited for Madeleine to take her turn in the game. "And she gave me a good scolding, too."

"Did you ever go back and beat up those Sarnia boys?" Charles asked loudly.

"Nope," his father replied with a chuckle. "We didn't beat them up. But Madeleine's

[*170*]

beating all of us at parcheesi. Look at what she's doing."

"I won!" Madeleine cried joyfully at that moment.

"You're a smart girl!" Edison exclaimed, reaching over and tweaking her nose. Getting to his feet, he picked Theodore up and held him high over his head. The little boy shouted with glee, and clutched his father's hair. Edison gave him a playful shake.

"Here, Mina, take this imp!" he said, dumping the child in his mother's lap. "I've brought work home from the laboratory, and I'd better get at it."

"Don't forget what day tomorrow is!" Charles shouted.

Edison laughed. "I never forget the Fourth of July," he replied, tousling the boy's hair. Then, sitting down at a big table, he pulled some papers toward him and went to work.

He was busy until long after midnight. But the next morning he was up before anyone else in the family. And when the children raced downstairs, he was waiting for them out-

[*171*]

*She noticed for the first time that his hair
was growing gray*

doors with piles of firecrackers and big boxes of torpedoes.

What a happy day that was! It did not end until the last Roman candle had scattered its colored stars against the evening sky.

Then the younger children were sent to bed. In a little while, Mrs. Edison went to say good night to them. When she came back again she found her husband working at his desk in the library. For a moment she stood in the doorway watching him.

His shoulders were stooped. And she noticed for the first time that his hair was growing gray.

"He seems tired," she thought. Crossing the room, she laid her hand on his shoulder. Edison looked up with a quick smile.

"It's been a fine day, hasn't it?" he asked.

Mrs. Edison nodded. "Tom, I wish you'd stop working so hard," she said. "You don't need to do it, and it's time you gave yourself a vacation. I—"

"Vacation!" Edison laughed. "Mina, dear, what on earth would I do with a vacation?

[*173*]

Why, I'm just starting experiments in the laboratory on a storage battery. It may take me years to learn how to make a *good* battery. And I have enough ideas for new inventions to last me the rest of my life."

"But aren't you ever going to stop working?" Mrs. Edison asked in dismay.

Edison patted her hand. "Of course I am," he said with a chuckle. "I'm going to stop on the day I'm a hundred years old."

And with another little chuckle, he turned back to his desk.

CHAPTER FIFTEEN

A Leader Among Men

IT WAS the night of October 21, 1929. Rain was falling on the town of Dearborn, Michigan and spattering against the windshield of Jake Mooney's taxicab.

Jake pulled his cab up before a little lunch shack near the edge of town. Trying to duck the raindrops, he ran into the shack and sat down on a stool before a grimy counter.

"A double hamburger with onion," he said to old Ma Henderson, who ran the shack. "Wow, I'm tired! This is the busiest day I've ever had."

Ma Henderson laid some chopped beef in a frying pan. "What's going on around here?" she asked as she put the pan on the stove. "Cars

[*175*]

have been buzzing past all day. And I've had six fancy-looking chauffeurs come in here since noon, asking the way to Henry Ford's museum in Greenfield Village."

Jake grinned. "Don't you listen to the radio, or read the papers, Ma?" he asked. "We got some of the biggest men in the country in town today. The big actor, Will Rogers, got here this morning. And Orville Wright, the fellow who made the flying machine, and President Hoover, and—"

"The President!" Ma Henderson exclaimed. "What's *he* doing here?"

"The same as all the others," Jake replied, biting into a dill pickle. "Going to the big banquet that Mr. Ford's giving for the man who invented those electric lights hanging from the ceiling."

Ma Henderson almost dropped the knife with which she was slicing an onion. "You mean Thomas Edison's here?" she asked in amazement. "Land sakes, Jake, he's the biggest man in the country!"

"That's right," Jake mumbled with his

[*176*]

mouth full. "Say, hurry up that hamburger, will you? Maybe I can pick up a few more customers."

Ma Henderson nodded and turned back to the stove.

Meanwhile, in the big hall in Henry Ford's museum, Thomas Edison and his wife sat side by side, at a long banquet table. All about them was a hum of talking, as men and women chatted together while waiters served a splendid dinner.

Now and then, Mrs. Edison looked proudly at her husband. When the dinner was almost over, her hand stole under the table and rested on his knee. With one finger she tapped out a message in the Morse code which he had taught her many years before.

"Your tie is crooked," she tapped. "Better fix it."

Edison touched his tie and winked at her. He looked out over the big room. At the other banquet tables, gay with flowers and shining silver. At the famous guests, who had come from many parts of the country and from foreign lands to honor him. He leaned toward his wife and a lock of snowy white hair fell across his forehead.

"This is an awful big hullabaloo for all these important folks to be making over an old fellow like me," he whispered, with a twinkle in his eyes. "I'm not worth it, Mina."

Mrs. Edison smiled. She disagreed with her husband. So did Herbert Hoover, the President of the United States. At that very moment he was getting to his feet, to make a speech praising the great inventor.

Edison settled back in his chair. He couldn't hear the President's words. And he was very tired. "No, I really haven't done half enough to deserve all this," he murmured to himself.

But even as the words passed his lips, things were happening all over the world which proved that he was wrong.

In Texas, a lonely rancher was talking by telephone with his daughter, who was in Maine. And he heard her voice as clearly as if she had been right beside him. Edison had made that possible!

A LEADER AMONG MEN

Near the island of Cuba, an American submarine was moving along far under the surface of the sea. The sailors knew that the lights in their big boat would not fail. For the electricity was being furnished by an Edison storage battery.

In a little Spanish village, children were shouting with laughter at an Edison motion picture. In the big city of London, a blind old English lady smiled with pleasure as she listened to the music which came from her Edison phonograph. And in a hospital in China, a doctor had just finished a dangerous operation which might have failed if he had not been helped by a brilliant Edison light.

No wonder President Hoover was speaking words of praise for Thomas Edison. No wonder celebrations were being held in Edison's honor all over the country.

But now the President had finished speaking and a hush had fallen over the museum hall in Greenfield Village. Suddenly Edison realized that everyone was looking at him. At that moment Mrs. Edison tugged at his coat.

[*179*]

And he knew that the time had come for him
to deliver the speech he had prepared.

Slowly the old gentleman rose to his feet.

Looking out at the crowd of famous guests, he
began to speak of the men who had helped him
in his work.

"In honoring me you are also honoring the vast army of thinkers and workers of the past, and those who are carrying on, without whom my work would have gone for nothing," he said. "If I have spurred men on to greater effort, and if our work has given even a measure of happiness in the world, I am content."

With warm words of thanks to his friend, Henry Ford, and to all who had helped in the splendid celebration, Edison sat down.

Then wave upon wave of wild applause arose from the big hall. Shouts and cheers made the rafters ring. Shouts and cheers that were heard by men and women listening to radios in every corner of the land, and across the sea.

People everywhere thought of all that Edison had done to bring them comfort and happiness. And they gave thanks that he had lived and worked for the good of all mankind. Thanks for Thomas Alva Edison, a leader among men.

SIGNATURE BOOKS are the true life-stories of real boys and girls who grew up to be famous men and women. These books tell of the many exciting adventures of those boys and girls when they were growing up, and what they did to make themselves remembered.

Leading authors and artists have worked together to give you the thrilling stories of these interesting people. If you liked the story you have just read, you will enjoy reading the books listed below and on the next page.

SIGNATURE BOOKS
"Names that Made History"

ENID LAMONTE MEADOWCROFT, *Supervising Editor*

THE STORY OF BUFFALO BILL
By Edmund Collier. *Illustrated by Nicholas Eggenhofer*

THE STORY OF CHRISTOPHER COLUMBUS
By Nina Brown Baker. *Illustrated by David Hendrickson*

THE STORY OF DAVY CROCKETT
By Enid LaMonte Meadowcroft. *Illustrated by C. B. Falls*

THE STORY OF THOMAS ALVA EDISON
By Enid LaMonte Meadowcroft. *Illustrated by Harve Stein*

THE STORY OF BENJAMIN FRANKLIN
By Enid LaMonte Meadowcroft. *Illustrated by Edward A. Wilson*

THE STORY OF ULYSSES S. GRANT
By Jeannette Covert Nolan.   *Illustrated by Lynd Ward*

THE STORY OF LAFAYETTE
By Hazel Wilson.   *Illustrated by Edy Legrand*

THE STORY OF ROBERT E. LEE
By Iris Vinton.   *Illustrated by John Alan Maxwell*

THE STORY OF ABRAHAM LINCOLN
By Nina Brown Baker.   *Illustrated by Warren Baumgartner*

THE STORY OF FLORENCE NIGHTINGALE
By Margaret Leighton.   *Illustrated by Corinne B. Dillon*

THE STORY OF LOUIS PASTEUR
By Alida Sims Malkus.   *Illustrated by Jo Spier*

THE STORY OF GEORGE WASHINGTON
By Enid LaMonte Meadowcroft. *Illustrated by Edward A. Wilson*

HANDSOME BOOKPLATES

*If you would like a set of bookplates, so that you can write
your own name in these books just the way the great signa-
tures are shown, send your name and address to*
SIGNATURE BOOKS, GROSSET & DUNLAP, INC.,
1107 BROADWAY, NEW YORK 10, N. Y.
*We will mail you, upon receipt of ten cents to pay the cost of
postage and handling, a set of handsomely designed
bookplates, each one different.*

1. Born in Milan, Ohio, February 11, 1847

2. Loses his hearing in train accident, 1859

3. Writes and prints the "Weekly Herald" on a moving train, 1862

4. His first invention— the automatic telegraph repeater, 1864

5. Sells stock-ticker patents for $40,000, New York, 1869

9. Invents the motion picture machine, West Orange, New Jersey, 1893

10. Dies in West Orange, New Jersey, October 18, 1931